TRUDY
AND
FAMILY

by
MARY ALICE FAID

LONDON
PICKERING & INGLIS LTD.

1970

PICKERING & INGLIS LTD.
29 LUDGATE HILL, LONDON, E.C.4
26 BOTHWELL STREET, GLASGOW, C.2

SBN 7208 2045 6

Printed in Great Britain by Northumberland Press Ltd., Gateshead

1

IT WAS A BEAUTIFUL DAY IN JULY AND Trudy Crawford, once Trudy Lawson, was enjoying a breathing space in her full and busy life.

She was sitting on the turf in a place called Shell Bay, where they had come for a holiday a fortnight ago. Today was their last day and if she didn't take this breathing space now it would be a long time before she got the chance again.

Still slim and girlish-looking in spite of being the mother of twins, she sat with her hands round her knees, her eyes gazing into space. For the time being she did not see the sandy bay nor the blue waves sparkling in the sun. She was even blind to the antics of the three figures at the edge of the water; one tall and lean—that was Derek, her husband—and two very small, tottery objects, one in blue waders, the other in red.

Matthew and Mark, now nineteen months old, were growing more obstreperous every day. The strongest, most tireless adults had been known to faint and fail when coping with them. Trudy herself could hardly have managed them had she not been well trained in 'boy taming' as a teacher before her marriage.

It seemed a very long time ago since her carefree girlhood days! True, she had had her ups and downs even then, but looking back she could see how free she had been. Free to come and go, to be herself with no one depending on her, and no one but herself suffering if she made some stupid mistake.

Now, her life was so inter-connected with Derek's and

the twins' that she was not a separate person any more. Trudy gave a tiny sigh. She had loved her freedom, especially during that year she had spent in a room of her own at the top of Cairn Castle in Martonbury. Yes, but even then there had been claims on her time and energies. One was not meant to live to oneself. It was good for you to have to think of others; it rounded out your personality, made you less selfish.

And it made the times you did get to yourself very precious indeed, like this afternoon, knowing that for a little while she was not needed and could indulge in what used to be her favourite pastime: dreaming.

What were the dreams that went through the mind of the fair-haired girl that summer afternoon? Romantic dreams of the past, of course, and all that had led up to her engagement and marriage. And dreams of even further back to the life at home with her parents and brothers and sister: David the eldest, the artistic one; Ping the live wire, and impetuous Nancy, now a nurse.

More recently, Trudy had realised her dream of getting them all together again, or almost so. In Hetherton where they lived, David was chief designer in a textile factory, while her mother and Ping had come to occupy the old house which used to belong to Meg Anderson, who was now married in Canada. Nancy spent some of her free time in Hetherton, too, so the Lawson family were united again, with all their 'attachments' as Ping called them. The present was very satisfactory, thank you; there seemed little left to wish for. But what would the future bring?

Trudy had experienced enough of life to know that things never stood still. No sooner had you made your little plans than something came along to upset them. There was no 'armour against fate' as the poem said. Yet, that was wrong. There *was* an armour against fate. She and those she loved had proved it time and again. It was an armour which you wore inside you, the sure knowledge

4

that, come what may, if you trusted in God he would give you strength to go through with it.

These were serious thoughts, typical of Trudy in certain moods. But she had her light-hearted phases, too, as all her friends were aware. Sometimes she still felt a lot younger than her years and found it difficult to behave like a mature married woman!

Derek was coming up the beach now, a wriggling bundle under each arm. Depositing the two infants on the sand, he sank down beside his wife.

"Exhausting work!" he panted. Then—"Why so thoughtful, Trudy?"

Her eyes came back from dreaming, to dwell on his lean, tanned face.

"Oh, I've just been thinking how much we have to be grateful for, you and I. You know, Derek, it does one good to get away like this. You can stand back and have a proper look at yourself."

"Oh, yes?" He sprinkled a handful of sand on her upturned palm and smiled up at her. "Most people would run a mile rather than look at themselves. I hope you liked what you saw? I know I do." He wiped off the sand and put a kiss on her palm instead.

She laughed. "Behave yourself, Derek Crawford! You've been married for four years now."

He sat up. "Yes, we have, haven't we? What's the date, Trudy?"

She suddenly remembered. "Derek, it's our Anniversary and we forgot all about it!"

She was aghast. It seemed unbelievable.

Derek seemed quite amused, however. "I'm glad we both forgot. If it had been me alone, I'd have been for it! Does this mean that we're getting used to each other, do you think?"

"It might be," was the solemn reply. "Please, don't let's get too used to each other. But I think those awful twins are to blame. They seem to crowd out everything else."

They sat contemplating the awful twins. Mark was staggering round with his pail, putting stones in it to hear the clink. Matthew, the docile one, was still seated, patting away at a small mound of sand. It was fine to see them both occupied and quiet, a state of affairs that happened all too seldom.

At that moment, Mark was seen to toddle towards his brother and fling his pail with its contents over his unoffending head. Both parents leapt to their feet, as Matthew let out an ear-splitting yell. Trudy lifted him up with soothing words, while Mark looked on unperturbed.

Derek shook his head at him. "You shouldn't have done that, old man!" But did a baby of one-and-a-half really know what he was doing? Being a father was no joke.

It was time now to go back to their boarding house to put the pair to bed and get packed for their departure next morning. No more dreaming, no more escape from housework and cooking and the routine tasks of every day. Face up to it, Trudy, your holiday is over.

"Not," said Derek that night as they packed the suitcases with the thousand and one things which babies require—"not that it has been much of a holiday for you, Trudy. Some day we'll park the twins with your mother and I'll take you away by yourself. Would you like that?"

"I would and I wouldn't," she admitted. "I'm afraid half of me would stay behind with them."

Next day a taxi came to take them to the station. What a business it was fitting themselves in with their countless packages, then out again at the station and into the train for Hetherton!

Fortunately, the train journey was short. On the way they looked after a twin apiece, pointing out passing objects

6

from the window; but Mark preferred to dig into Trudy's handbag and Matthew to pull at Derek's tie. Now and again they would get restless and when put on their feet, they explored the carriage, placing podgy hands on the knees of the passengers, and gazing solemnly up into their faces. People were very nice to them, but Trudy was glad when the train reached Hetherton.

"Well, here we are home again!" she exclaimed.

"You sound quite happy about it," remarked Derek as he proceeded to unload, bag and baggage.

"I'm always happy to get back home."

And indeed it was a pleasant place to come home to. The station itself was in the old village of Hetherton, a picturesque spot with white cottages and pretty gardens. Up the hill a new town had grown, with modern houses and shops, a new school and a church. There was also the mission hall in the field beside the palatial home of that strong-minded lady, Mrs. Scott Brown. Trudy felt she could have written a book about the building of that hall. A book? She had hardly time to write out her shopping lists, let alone a book.

Through the station gate a stout man with a jolly face strode forward to help them with their luggage. It was 'Tam the Taxi'.

"Mrs. Lawson told me you would likely be coming with this train," he informed them. "The taxi's waiting."

"Good!" breathed Derek. "We certainly need it! These kids weigh a ton."

"Real roly-polys," commented Tam. "They're a good advertisement for Hetherton."

All the children here were rosy cheeked and healthy. There was something about the air. It was an ideal place to bring up a family and Trudy never stopped being grateful that Derek had been appointed to open a branch Bank here.

When they reached the Bank building, Mrs. Lawson was

on the lookout and came hurrying to help them out of the taxi. She took one of the twins in her arms.

"They look well! You too, Trudy. You needed that holiday."

Derek was taking the luggage upstairs assisted by Tam. Their flat was above the Bank with a wonderful view of the surrounding countryside.

It was some time before everything was transported and Trudy got a chance to view her house after their fortnight's absence. It still gave her a thrill when she came back to it, remembering the day when as a new bride she had been carried across the threshold by her adoring husband. Four years of ups and downs, of falling out and falling in again, though the 'outs' were few and far between. Never a dull moment in all the four years.

At the first opportunity, Trudy took a peep into each of the rooms; the two bedrooms, the lounge with its wine coloured carpet and grey-blue suite, and the living-room, brightly decorated in lime green and royal blue. Then through to the kitchen where the curtains with the seagulls still hung, though they were getting a little shabby now. But everything else was bright and sparkling as ever, including the whistling kettle which had dominated their newly married lives.

"I couldn't imagine a more perfect house than this!" Trudy exclaimed, as she took up the twins one after the other to show them the view of fields and rolling hills.

Mrs. Lawson, busy at the cooker, smiled to herself. It was just like Trudy to give vent to her feelings when she was pleased and happy. About her dissatisfactions she was more reserved, which was as it should be.

Derek had started to open the letters which had arrived during their absence. There was one from Nancy saying that she hoped to come and see them in a fortnight's time. Another from Ping, who was helping to run a seaside mission, announced that he, too, would be home soon.

8

"Good! We'll have a proper family gathering," crowed Trudy. "What other letters are there, Derek?"

"Oh, just one from Bank headquarters on business," he replied in a secretive voice, and thrust the letter into his pocket. During tea he was very quiet but Trudy said nothing, being fully occupied attending to the twins. They had a high chair apiece and had to be strictly supervised, otherwise their food was apt to land everywhere except in their mouths.

There was the usual rush to get them bathed and into bed, and then came the unpacking. This completed, Mrs. Lawson prepared to go home and Derek accompanied her down the road. Trudy felt she could relax at last. This was the time of day when she and Derek usually had a 'heart-to-heart' session. Of course if the babies were restless or anyone came in, it was impossible; but they tried to make it a rule to keep this time to discuss the happenings of the day. So, though drowsy, she kept awake till she heard his key in the door.

She noticed at once that he looked worried, for a sixth sense had grown between them.

"Tired?" he asked, smiling at her.

"Not so very. Derek, you might as well tell me. What was in that letter from the Bank?"

He flushed. "Oh that! Nothing much. I'll tell you some other time."

But she was convinced that the letter had contained something important. "Why not tell me now? You know that waiting is a thing I hate."

He smiled. It was true; his Trudy was always eager to get to the heart of things.

"Oh well, I see you're determined," he gave in, taking the letter from his pocket. "Read it for yourself."

As Trudy read, her expression lost its brightness and became one of dismay.

9

2

THE NEWS WAS TOTALLY UNEXPECTED. DEREK had not applied for promotion; he was perfectly content with his post in Hetherton. But this was promotion none the less. The company's bank in Firton, a large town ten miles away, was a very important one and Derek had been appointed manager.

Seeing his wife's expression of dismay, he demanded:

"Well, aren't you in favour? This will mean more money for us, Trudy."

"What's money?" she asked stormily. "They might have left us in peace! Firton is such a dirty, smoky place; the babies would have no chance there. Do you have to accept, Derek?"

"I expect so." Like every other man with a home to keep up, he was anxious to get on in his career. "Come on, let's sit down and talk it over."

Seated on the sofa in the lounge, he put his arm round her.

"I am as much against a change as you are, Trudy. If you have insurmountable objections, I'll turn down the offer."

After a moment's reflection, she replied, "No, Derek; it would mean frustration for you. You're fit for the responsibility and I wouldn't hold you back. But do we need to live in Firton? There's a good bus service from here. Couldn't you travel daily, as Ping does to college?"

"Possibly I could," he replied thoughtfully.

Her spirits rose again. "Then there need be no removal.

I simply couldn't give up this flat, Derek. It would break my heart!"

"Would it, Trudy?" He gazed at her sadly. "But you're forgetting something. The flat goes with the Bank. Whoever takes my place will have to live in it."

Down crashed her hopes again. Some intruder to occupy this darling house of hers—how dare they!

"It's not fair," she burst out. "We've done so much here; it belongs to us. Nobody else could possibly feel the same about it. Derek, mightn't there be a chance that whoever comes might not want it?"

"There's a chance, certainly," he reflected, "but don't depend on it. I'll try to find out. In the meantime we'll just have to have patience."

But Trudy felt rebellious. Not for herself; she would have lived anywhere with Derek. It was the health of her babies she was worried about. She had seen the Firton Bank. It was in a street full of traffic and the fumes from cars and lorries. The windows of the Bank house were always sooty and there was no garden. Yet that was where they would have to live, for they had no money to buy a house in the suburbs.

After Derek had departed for his duties next morning, she had little time to ponder, for the twins had to be dressed and fed and put into their play-pen. They were at the stage when, if let loose, they would get into all sorts of mischief. Mark had been known to open the sideboard door and smash some of her good wedding china before anyone could stop him. Matthew would gleefully pull a book from a shelf and make hay of the pages. A pail of water on the floor was never safe and the coal scuttle was a constant temptation. No matter how careful you were to keep things out of their way, they would always find a loophole. So, unless you could keep an eagle eye on all their doings, the play-pen it had to be.

No sooner were they left inside with their toys than

Trudy was summoned to the telephone. She guessed it would be her sister-in-law, Esther, and so it turned out to be. David's wife, who had been her friend since schooldays, lived in a bungalow called 'Two Ways,' not far away. She had two children, too, both girls.

Trudy Anne, who was still referred to as the 'Wee Precious', was due to start school after the holidays and Margaret was about two years younger. Having children had brought Esther and Trudy even closer together. Their friendship was founded on mutual help and companionship, but perhaps the strongest bond between them was their belief in the Christian ideal. Together they had grown to womanhood holding firm to their faith, and sometimes it had not been easy.

"Is that you, Trudy?" asked Esther on the line. "Oh good, you got home safely. How are the twins?"

"Riotous as usual, thanks. And your little lambs?"

"Frisky," was the reply. "Not very popular with David just now! They've totally claimed his studio in the garden; it's quite put him off painting. But he's on to another tack now—pottering."

"Pottering?" was the puzzled enquiry.

Her friend laughed. "I mean 'potting', of course. You know what a potter is. Well, he says he's going to be one."

"But he's a designer," argued Trudy.

"Yes, he says that's his bread and butter, but potting is to be his jam. He's looking for an old building to make into a pottery."

Well, well, what would that brother of hers be up to next?

"Tell me about it this afternoon, Esther. I'll bring the infants along about three. I've got news."

"Bad or good?" asked the other.

"Definitely bad. Be ready with support and sympathy. I'd tell you now, but there's a rumpus going on in the play-pen, a duet of screams. Do you hear them?"

"I should just think I do," declared Esther.

Trudy hurriedly put down the phone and rushed to the rescue. Mark had attacked his brother with a drumstick, the offended Matthew had started to roar; then Mark himself joined in, in sympathy. Trudy decided they were both tired, having been awake since six o'clock, so she put Mark in the big pram in the garden to sleep, and tucked Matthew into his cot in the room. To separate them was the best way to get peace.

In the early afternoon she put them both in the pram and started off for Esther's house. The sun was shining and the air was full of the perfume of roses which were growing profusely in the bungalow gardens. Normally she would have enjoyed every minute of the walk, but the problem of their future was still in the forefront of her mind.

Esther's two girls were playing in the garden under the care of Mrs. Burton, who came to help daily. She and her neighbours, who lived in the tenement overlooking Mrs. Scott Brown's, were regular attenders at the mission. She turned a smiling face to Trudy:

"I needn't ask you if your holiday agreed with you!" She greeted her. "You look blooming, and so do the bairns."

The two little girls came running up to inspect their twin cousins, a constant source of wonder to them. They were not unlike twins themselves, for Margaret was big for her age and Trudy Anne was small and delicately made.

"Please, Aunt Trudy, can I lift Mark up to nurse him?" asked the elder.

"He'd topple you over," was the smiling reply, "but I'll leave them both here with you in their pram, if Mrs. Burton doesn't object?"

"Of course not. They'll be no trouble," declared the other.

The door was open, so Trudy went inside. Esther was in the lounge resting. Though her health was better these days, she still tired easily. Springing up, she threw her arms round her friend.

"Lovely to see you again, Trudy!"

"And lovely to be back." The bond between these two grew stronger with the years. After the first flow of talk, Trudy went on:

"The most upsetting thing has happened, Esther!" And she divulged the news in Derek's letter.

"You mean you'll be leaving Hetherton? But you can't, Trudy. Everything in this place would fall to pieces!"

"I doubt it," was the rueful reply. "It's me that would fall to pieces. Derek says if the new man doesn't want our flat, they'll probably allow us to stay on, but I can't imagine anyone turning it down, can you?"

"Not unless it was someone with a large family who needed more room. When will you know, Trudy?"

"I've no idea. Talk about suspense! Nobody knows this but you, Esther. I shan't even tell Mum till we know one way or the other. She has enough to worry about, with things going up in price the way they are. She and Ping are pretty scrimped, you know, and she won't take a penny piece from any of us."

"I know. She says that people with growing children need all they've got. True enough, I suppose. I know I ought to be able to save, Trudy, but I'm the world's worst manager! I think that's why David has started this craze for pottery, to make a little extra. He's looking for a place to instal a kiln, so that he can work there in his spare time."

Trudy shook her head dubiously. "Sounds a bit hare-brained to me. You've got wonderful patience with David and his crazes."

Trudy's visit was short; there was so much to do at home. In any case these two saw each other nearly every day, so there was no need for a long stay. How long would this happy state of affairs last? Trudy asked herself the question as she carted off the twins, each consuming a rather damp rusk from Esther's supply.

She was hurrying along, eager to get home, when an ancient car, driven by a chauffeur, came alongside and stopped at the kerb. Oh dear, of all days to meet Mrs. Scott Brown! Trudy was obliged to wait while the commanding old dame opened the window and spoke:

"So you are home again! Did you enjoy your holiday?"

"Yes thank you, very much," was the reply.

The lady leant out to peer at the twins, whose faces were crumby with rusk.

"I don't know how you cope with them. Let me see them properly. My sight is failing."

Trudy wheeled the pram close.

"Alike as two peas. Put one of them on my lap, will you?"

Rather fearfully, Trudy complied, wondering if her friend had ever nursed a child in her life before. The baby smiled serenely up into the stern old face and lisped:

"Gran-gran!"

She was delighted. "An intelligent infant. Which one is it?"

"That's Matthew. He's quieter than Mark."

"Yes, he's very sweet. I must get to know him better. What about coming home with me now?"

Trudy explained that it wasn't possible. "Some other afternoon perhaps?"

The other frowned. "You refuse me so often! I wonder I have anything to do with you."

At one time, Trudy would have been taken aback, but now she was not afraid to speak her mind to the forthright old lady.

"You never give me any warning," she replied with a smile. "You're just a dictator."

15

Mrs. Scott Brown chuckled. "Of course I'm a dictator. I usually get away with it, too. But not with you, that's why I like you. Oh well, another day. By the way, I have just had word from Roy, your future brother-in-law. He is coming to stay next week. I gather your sister will be on holiday, too."

Trudy nodded. "I had a letter last night from Nancy. How nice for them both!"

She was very pleased about the arrangement. A year ago Nancy had become engaged to Mrs. Scott Brown's nephew, Roy Melrose, who lived in Hampstead, near London.

They had first met in Broomfield garden. Trudy remembered the day perfectly, for it was on the first anniversary of the opening of the new hall. She and Nancy, on their way to the hall, had stopped to look at the flowers in the garden, when Roy and his aunt appeared. They were invited in and Trudy could still recall the young man's admiring glance when introduced to her attractive, dark-eyed sister.

But Matthew, growing impatient, was squirming and kicking his fat little legs on the old lady's lap.

"Here," she said, "you'd better take him. I'm not really used to babies. To tell the truth, I'm rather afraid of them."

Trudy transferred Matthew to the pram and went on her way, encouraging the twins to wave their hands as the car passed them. For once they both obliged and were accorded an approving smile.

When Trudy reached the Bank, Derek was just locking up for the day. Eva Somers, his chief assistant, was there too. She came running to meet them, her pretty face bright with welcome. Eva adored the twins and often took charge of them in the evenings to let Derek and Trudy out together.

They had got to know Eva many years ago, when she

was a tiny slip of a girl on holiday like themselves on the island of Barone. Ping had been Eva's hero then, and it looked as if he still was.

Her blue eyes were sparkling. "Oh, how I've missed you all! I had a letter from Ping, Trudy. He seems to be enjoying the seaside mission. When he goes back, I might go too. My holidays are due in August."

Up in the flat, Trudy bustled to and fro. "I meant to be home much sooner," she told Derek, "but we met Mrs. Scott Brown. She tells me Roy is coming for a visit while Nancy's here. Isn't that super?"

"Yes, but it strikes me you won't see much of Nancy. These loving couples never seem to notice anyone but each other."

"Derek Crawford, it's not so long since you were a half of a loving couple yourself!"

"I hope I still am." He put his arm round her, rubbing his cheek against hers. "Trudy, have you thought over what we were discussing last night?"

She nodded. "I've thought of nothing else. Have you accepted yet, Derek?"

"No, but I'm writing to the head office tonight—with your permission."

"You have it. It would be wrong of me to stand in your way. If we're to lose this house it can't be helped. We've been through bad times before, Derek. We'll just have to put our armour on."

"Yes, dear. What armour is that?" he enquired.

"Our armour against fate. Our trust in God to see us through."

He smiled in complete understanding.

3

TRUDY HAD TOLD DEREK THAT WAITING WAS a thing she hated. It was a characteristic that had its good points and its bad. If one was too patient and waited too long, opportunities were missed. On the other hand, if you rushed at things or rushed other people, it often led to failure and frustration.

Derek, who was the slow kind, seemed quite content to jog along waiting for news about the house, but though he was told that he would hear from his successor, the word was long in coming.

Whatever happened, he was now definitely committed to starting in the Firton Bank in September. It was a blow to Eva, who had got on so well with her 'boss'.

"Can't I come to work in Firton too?" she asked.

"Much better not," Derek told her. "Later on, if there's a vacancy, I'll recommend you. But you will be very useful here. This Mr. Rice who is taking my place will need someone who knows the ropes."

Eva looked glum. "'Rice'? What a name! I'm sure not to like him. Rice is my most unfavourite pudding."

Derek laughed. "He'll probably be much nicer than his name."

"Is there a Mrs. Rice?" asked Eva.

"That's what we're waiting to hear."

When Trudy at length confided in her mother, Mrs. Lawson took the news calmly, as she took everything.

"It wasn't to be expected that Derek would stay in the same place for long," she commented. "The Bank know what they're doing to promote him. Be thankful it's no further away than Firton. He'll still be able to run the mission here."

They went on to talk about Nancy, who was expected to arrive next day.

"Can you meet her at the station, Trudy? She'll have plenty to tell you."

Trudy was delighted to oblige. When the time came, she prevailed upon Derek to look after the twins, as it was his Saturday holiday.

"If you're quite sure you'll be able to cope, Derek?"

"Sure I will; I'm their father amn't I? I'll simply plump them into their play-pen and forget about them. I've got some writing to do."

Trudy doubted if it would be so simple, but said no more. For her it was a lovely free afternoon. She walked down the hill to the station, a cardigan over her summer frock, head bare, her feet clad in white sandals. She would have felt very young and carefree, had it not been for this awful uncertainty about where they were going to live.

The train was a little late, but she did not mind waiting in the pretty little station, chatting with the station master, Rob Macadam. He and the other village people were a different type from the people who lived on the hill. For a time she and Derek had found the village folk a closed community, who resented the newcomers. A different spirit was growing now, chiefly due to the 'Love Your Neighbour Guild' run by the young men and girls of the mission.

In a very short time she heard the train approaching and when it stopped at the platform she looked eagerly for her sister. At last she spied her, but Nancy was not alone. A very tall, fair young man with slightly stooping shoulders was helping her to alight. It was Roy Melrose, and his mother was there, too. Trudy had not seen her since her visit to London more than two years ago. She was rather a stately lady, but her manner had been kindly enough to the stranger who had never been in London before.

Trudy kissed Nancy, who was looking radiant, and shook hands with the other two. For Roy she had a specially warm spot. She recalled how thrilled she had been on the day he took her to see 'Keats Grove' in Hampstead, where the poet had written his 'Ode to the Nightingale'. He seemed to know instinctively what would appeal to her.

His blue eyes twinkled as he held her hand.

"We meet again, Trudy! Have you written any poetry lately?"

She shook her head. "I'm afraid I've forgotten how. Poetry and babies don't mix!"

Mrs. Scott Brown's ancient car had drawn up at the station gate driven by her chauffeur. Roy helped his mother aboard, asking:

"Nancy and Trudy, would you like a lift?"

Trudy said that as their mother's house was close by, they could quite well walk. Roy, obviously unwilling to leave Nancy, remarked ruefully:

"Well, as I can't be in two places at once, I'd better go with Mother. May I visit Ardenlea tonight?"

"Yes, please do," they both urged.

Mrs. Melrose called from the car:

"Come along, Roy; it won't do to keep Aunt Charlotte waiting."

Pressing Nancy's hand, he got into the car which glided away from them towards Broomfield. Trudy took Nancy's case, and they walked on.

"I like Roy," she told her sister. "I'm looking forward to having him for a brother-in-law. Any chance of it being soon?"

"Not a hope," was the gloomy reply. "It's nice being engaged, Trudy, but we hardly ever see each other."

"I know how it feels. Derek and I were the same, but we got through. Good thing you've got your nursing, same as I had my teaching."

"Yes, I'm kept busy, fortunately." She gave Trudy a smiling glance. "I must say, Trudy, marriage agrees with you. Four years now! By the way I meant to send you a card for your Anniversary but I completely forgot."

Trudy laughed. "I can't blame you; we completely forgot ourselves."

Nancy couldn't believe it. "I hope that's not because you're disillusioned?"

"By no means. It's the twins who crowd everything else out. We're learning how to be parents and it's not easy."

When they reached Ardenlea their mother was at the door. She greeted her younger daughter fondly. For a time Nancy had withdrawn herself from her mother's love and it had been a miserable time for them both, but now they were close again and there was no more holding back.

Trudy said she ought really to be getting back to the twins, but she could not resist the offer of a cup of tea. First, she took Nancy's case up to her room.

Ardenlea was a typical semi-detached villa built in Victorian times. Downstairs there was a living-room and kitchen with a medium sized room at the back and the 'big' room at the front, with an oriel window. The upper floor contained three apartments of which one was Ping's study. There were also two attic rooms with skylight windows.

When Meg Anderson and her mother lived in the house, it had been a dreary place with dark woodwork and wallpapers, but all that had been changed. The staircase was painted a gleaming white and the rooms decorated in bright colourings. Most of these changes had been accomplished by the men folk of the family working overtime, and how worth while it had been!

They sat in the big room with the sun shining in and drank the tea served from a silver teapot in fluted cups which were part of Mrs. Lawson's wedding china.

"Aren't we stylish?" remarked Nancy. "You'd think it was a special occasion."

"It is a special occasion," declared her mother. "I don't often have my two girls all to myself like this." She studied their faces thinking what a contrast they still were, these two, though now so mature and responsible: Trudy with her shining red-gold hair and dreamy eyes, Nancy dark and impulsive.

Mrs. Lawson never ceased to thank God that her elder daughter had found happiness in marriage and motherhood; and that the younger one had also bright prospects ahead. Though the stormy Nancy would always attract trouble because of her temperament, her life was still guided by Christian principles and what more steadying influence could a girl have?

Involuntarily, her mother glanced up at one of her most cherished possessions which hung on the wall above the sideboard. It was a large plaque given to her last summer by their old friend Brian Clyde, the 'Artist Preacher'. He had made it himself, firing it in the kiln of the Martonbury Art School, where he taught painting and pottery.

In the middle of the plaque a mother and her baby were depicted with the verse from Proverbs: 'Train up a child in the way he should go, and when he is old, he will not depart from it'. Round the rim of the plaque were listed, according to age, the names of all Mrs. Lawson's children and grand-children: David, Trudy, Nancy, Ping, Trudy Anne, Margaret, Matthew and Mark.

Trudy smiled when she saw the direction of her mother's gaze.

"Quite a crowd of us now! Dear knows what the last two are doing at this moment. I think I'd better go and see."

She was no sooner on her feet, however, than they caught

sight of Derek wheeling the big pram in at the gate. His face was red and his hair all ruffled; he looked at his last gasp.

They all surged out to the garden.

"Anything wrong?" asked Trudy.

"Wrong? What an age you've been!" he exclaimed. "These two have sapped my strength."

"So you didn't get your writing done," observed his wife.

"Writing! I didn't dare take my eyes off them for a moment. To bring them out was the only way to get peace!"

Trudy regarded her sons critically. "Well, you might have washed their faces first." Matthew's was streaked with jam and Mark's bore traces of chocolate.

"I did enough," grunted Derek. "Anyhow, they wouldn't have let me."

"Don't worry, they're perfect as they are," said Nancy, bending over the pram. "What utter darlings! Come to Aunt Nancy!" and she took them up, one on each arm.

"You're welcome to them," pronounced their father. Mrs. Lawson took him inside for a cup of tea while Nancy continued to amuse the twins in the garden. She adored babies and in her teens had liked nothing better than to wheel out the neighbours' children in their prams. Now that she had nieces and nephews of her own, she got plenty of practice.

"Still, I'll not be satisfied," she told Trudy, "till I have a family of my own. Shall I tell you my dreams for the future?"

Trudy said she would love to hear them.

"Well, perhaps I ought not to mention it, but you do know that Roy's Aunt Charlotte has made him her heir? Broomfield is to be his, but he's expected to come and live in it, me too. When I saw that house first I was thrilled with it—remember?"

Trudy nodded. "You said you'd love to live in a house like that some day. Also you said—'Small chance!'"

"Little I knew. I also remarked that it would be a grand family house and I still think that. In fact, I'd like to see the house and garden simply filled with children."

"Dear me. All your own? I find that two's enough."

"Not all my own," reflected Nancy. "Just two or three. The rest would be orphans and children deprived of love. I'd give them lots of it and they would grow up strong and happy. It's all very much in the future of course," she broke off.

"Something to aim for, all the same. I suppose Roy would agree to all this?"

"I haven't consulted him, but I'm sure he would, once we're married. But that can't be for a while. There's his mother, you see. She's a widow and she would miss him."

Trudy studied her sober face. "So that's what's holding him back. What a pity."

"Roy," Nancy went on, "has supported his mother for years. They've been all in all to each other. She is quite a nice person, Trudy, but I—I don't think she approves of me."

"Oh, nonsense. I should think any mother would be glad to get a girl like you for a daughter-in-law. You're good-looking, you're practical, and you have plenty of common sense."

This eulogy seemed to amuse Nancy. "Thank you, kind madam. You weren't always so complimentary! But seriously, I think Mrs. Melrose would grudge Roy to any girl, no matter how perfect. Am I very wicked to say so?"

"Not if it's true. But perhaps you're just imagining it, Nancy. Anyhow, you've got a chance to get really friendly with her while you're here. Let her see that Roy has made a good choice."

Nancy made a wry face. "Sure, I'll be on my best behaviour, but the poor lad is going to be pulled both ways, I know. You saw how it was at the station. I do wish Aunt Charlotte had asked him here by himself."

Trudy had got the impression that Mrs. Scott Wood had not expected Roy's mother at all, but she said nothing. She only hoped that Nancy was not going to experience more heartache. She had had quite enough.

The two girls had been so intent on their conversation that the twins had been forgotten. In the space of two minutes they had made rapid progress towards the gate and Mark was giving loud chuckles of glee. A thin, bronzed young man with clear grey eyes, who had arrived unnoticed, had snatched him up and was practically throwing him into the air.

Trudy ran towards them. "Ping Lawson, what sort of treatment is that to give your nephew?"

"He loves it," declared her brother. "Come on, number two, would you like a go?" But Matthew let out such a furious yell that Ping rapidly replaced him on the ground.

"Number one is much more sporting! I guess he must be Mark. He's a right bubble—look how fat he is. Matthew's just a squeak. I shall call them Bubble and Squeak."

"You'll do no such thing," protested their mother. "Derek and I have vowed there are to be no nick-names."

"You are the one to talk!" Ping drew himself up and thumped his chest. "What about poor me? Haven't I been afflicted with a nick-name since my infant days?"

It was quite true. Ping's real name was Peter, but though they had made several attempts to use it, they never succeeded for long. Even though he had been an 'M.A.' for a year now, the old nick-name stuck.

At that moment Derek emerged from the house to give Ping a warm greeting.

"You're just in time to take the service tomorrow morning," he told him. "Good practice for you, Ping!"

4

ONE THING THAT SUNDAY ALWAYS BROUGHT
was a change of routine and that was one reason, though not
the only one, that made Trudy look forward to it.

During summer, there was no evening service at the
mission, but the Sunday School and morning service went
on all the year round. If Derek could not attend in person,
he was always able to find a substitute.

As for Trudy, she usually contrived to get out on a
Sunday morning. One of the Sunday School teachers,
Peggy Paterson, now Mrs. Andy Carson, was only too willing to look after the twins. This Sunday, she arrived at
the house in good time. The twins were already settled for
their forenoon nap, one in the house, the other in the
garden.

"They might sleep till we get back," Trudy told the good-
natured Peggy.

"I hope they don't," was the forthright reply, "they're
more fun awake."

"And more bother, too!"

"Ach, I don't call that bother. I only wish I had some
kids of my own."

"You will have some day, I'm sure. Don't be in too big
a hurry! What would I do without you on Sunday mornings?" asked Trudy as she set a white straw hat on her
newly brushed hair. Hats were kept for Sundays and
special occasions. As a rule she preferred to go bare-
headed.

She set out with Derek for the hall, as the sun burst
out from a bank of cloud.

26

"Going to be another fine day," she said, taking her husband's arm. "I hope there will be a good turn-out."

Although the new church in the scheme was now completed, many people still adhered to the mission. There was room for both, each working in harmony to extend the Kingdom of Jesus Christ. As Derek often remarked, the fields were all white and the reapers were all too few.

In the sun, the mission building gleamed cheerfully. Opened more than two years ago, it still looked new and welcoming, standing in the big field next to the mansion of Mrs. Scott Brown. Dozens of worshippers could be seen making their way to it this fine morning.

Trudy recalled the thrill they had all felt on the night when Brian Clyde performed the opening ceremony. His text from Psalm 122 had been: 'I was glad when they said unto me, Let us go into the House of the Lord'.

"In this building," Brian foretold, "the sad ones will find comfort, the weak ones will find strength, and those who are lost will find the way."

His words had come true, as Trudy and Derek and scores of others could testify.

Another wonderful thing was how they had managed to pay off every penny of debt. At last, as Derek put it, the Broomfield Mission was 'washing its face'. However, with expenses going up, they dare not relax their efforts. It was a case of 'To the Work, to the Work', without cessation. Though it was supposed to be old-fashioned nowadays to talk about the 'Devil', there was no doubt he was ready to step in the minute you stopped working for God.

Smiles and greetings were exchanged with their friends as they entered the cheerful building with its many windows and pale primrose walls. Derek was soon on the platform and with him Ping, still a thin, rather gangling figure, but broadening out into manhood's stature.

At the organ, Esther played an opening voluntary, a

27

simple piece rather spoiled, unfortunately, by the breathless wheezing of the instrument. They badly needed a new organ, but that would have to wait.

The hymn with which they started was an appropriate one: 'Summer Suns are glowing over Land and Sea'. After that, Ping, who was well known to everybody, took over the service. He stood erect, surveying them with a strangely compelling glance for one so young. Great things were expected of Ping. From a small boy, his great ambition was to be a preacher like his hero, Brian Clyde. Now that that aim was well within his grasp, the impetus was stronger than ever. His address was direct and simple, the theme taken from Romans 1.16: 'I am not ashamed of the Gospel of Jesus Christ'.

Young people today, he began, were beginning to realise that the material things of the world were not enough. Without some spiritual content their lives were empty. Some of them were flying to strange cults, a few of which had something in their favour. The cult of meditation, for instance, had its good points, and the idea of Love in everything was on the right lines, too.

"But," he went on, "none of these in themselves are enough. We have them all and much, much more in our own Christian religion, founded as it is on the Cross of Jesus Christ. This is a Gospel which has stood the test of time. It has changed men's lives and been their inspiration throughout the ages. Instead of being ashamed of this faith, we should glory in it. We should proclaim it from the housetops!"

As always, Ping's words carried conviction and his hearers were much moved. Here was no tired, ageing speaker with his mind in the past, but a vital young man carrying the torch of faith into the future, imparting hope and encouragement in a day of disillusion.

Trudy's heart was full as she listened. Glancing at her mother beside her, she saw a tear glistening on her cheek.

No wonder Mrs. Lawson's heart was touched, for it was due to her teaching and example that Ping was able to preach these truths today.

Ping's message was taken up in the hymn which followed:

'I'm not ashamed to own my Lord, or to defend His cause,
Maintain the honour of His word, the glory of His cross.'

When they came to the chorus the congregation sang with renewed fervour:

'At the cross! at the cross! where I first saw the light,
And the burden of my heart rolled away,
It was there by faith I received my sight,
And now I am happy all the day!'

At the end of the service Trudy hurried to the door to get the chance to speak to her friends as they came out. Practically every one of the people was known to her and their circumstances as well. In spite of her motherly duties she had made the effort to keep in touch with them all. She would not be able to do this if they went to live in Firton. There would be no one there to take charge of the twins; she might even have to cut herself off from the mission altogether.

These gloomy thoughts were dispersed by the approach of Mrs. Cooper and her husband the schoolmaster. The pair had been very kind to Eva Somers when she lost her grandmother as a child. Eva still lived with them, for her own mother, a widow, had married again.

Some two years back, however, Eva's mother had claimed her and taken her off to London. That was a bleak time for Ping! But Eva had come back, preferring the simple life in Hetherton, to a more luxurious one in the big world.

Did Eva ever regret her decision? Trudy often wondered. So much could have been hers, a glittering marriage, a chance to go abroad and to enjoy all the things that money could buy. Perhaps it was too much to expect her to remain content with the life here?

As she stood chatting with the Coopers, Trudy saw Eva herself coming along with Ping, and there was certainly no regret on her piquant, smiling face. Ping was looking happy, too.

"What do you think, Trudy, Eva is offering to give up her holiday to work at the seaside mission. Do you think I should let her?"

"You'll have to. I insist," laughed Eva. "I'd be lonely going away by myself, anyway."

"I thought you might be joining your mother," Trudy put in. "Isn't she in this country just now?"

Eva's face changed. "Yes, she is, but she says she has washed her hands of me. However," her chin went up, "I have got other friends!"

"You certainly have," Ping assured her.

Roy Melrose and Nancy were just behind them. Neither Mrs. Melrose nor Aunt Charlotte had come, so the two were alone for a time at least. Trudy was glad. She believed that young couples in love should be left to work out their own destinies. She felt so much older and wiser about 'young couples' now that she was married herself.

Watching them go down the hill arm in arm, Nancy dark and sturdily built, Roy so tall and distinguished looking, she hoped the time would soon come when they would be man and wife.

"Why so thoughtful?" asked a voice at her side. It was David, the handsome one of the Lawson family, though to Trudy's mind he would look much better without that tuft of hair on his chin!

"Hello, David! I'm waiting for Esther. Is she coming?"

"Just tidying up her music. Has she told you about my great new plans, Trudy?"

"You mean about starting a pottery? Yes, she has."

"Someday I hope to make it a full-time business," he went on enthusiastically. "No set hours, my own master. Imagine that, Trudy!"

"Yes, but it's very much up in the air, isn't it? You haven't even got a place for it."

"Something's sure to turn up," he declared.

"And what will you use for money?"

He glowered at her. "That's right, throw cold water over my schemes. Esther doesn't do that."

"Esther's too patient with you. But don't think I'm against this, David. It's only that you're not very practical."

Just then Esther came out in a hurry. "Oh dear, it's time I was back to take over from Mrs. Burton." She took Trudy's arm and the two went off talking earnestly. "I thought Ping was just wonderful this morning, Trudy; he's going to be a great preacher. By the way, have you heard anything about what's happening to your house?"

"Not a word. It's maddening, being kept waiting; like living on the edge of a precipice. I simply can't settle to anything."

Two days later, the postman handed Trudy a letter in a strange handwriting. Excitedly, she ran with it to Derek, who was having breakfast. He took it from her with that slow, deliberate air of his.

"This is probably It," he said.

"Oh Derek, open it, quick!"

But as usual he refused to be rushed. Whereas she would have slit the envelope with her thumb, he had to look for the paper knife. When eventually it was found, the letter was opened and the contents revealed.

Mr. Rice, it appeared, hoped to take up his duties in September. Regarding the house, he would be paying a visit to Hetherton on the 15th instant, accompanied by his wife. She was very anxious to view the flat to decide if it would be suitable for them to take over. He was theirs, very sincerely, 'James B. Rice'.

"The fifteenth!" exclaimed Trudy, aghast. "Why, that's today!"

"You're right. The letter must have been delayed. Well, the sooner the better," observed Derek.

"No such thing! Don't you realise the house is not ready for inspection? Look at the windows—filthy! The kitchen's in a frightful muddle, the furniture needs polishing. There's finger-marks everywhere!"

"Calm down," advised her husband. "Getting in a flap won't help."

"All very well for you," gulped Trudy. "It's not your department. If I'd only had proper warning, I'd have had everything shining."

Derek's eyes twinkled. "Why bother? The worse the place looks, the less Mrs. Rice will like it. You don't want her to like it, do you?"

"No," she admitted, "but I don't wish her to think I'm a slovenly housewife, either. And oh, Derek, what shall I do about the twins? They're sure to be on their worst behaviour."

"I don't see that that should worry her," declared the dense creature. "They're not her twins."

Exasperated, Trudy shooed him away from the table and started to clear it at top speed. Never had the dishes been washed so quickly. She let the twins howl away in their cots till she was ready to bathe them and give them their cereal. Then into the play-pen they went, while she skimmed round giving things a 'lick and a promise', for that was all there was time for.

5

IT WAS NEARLY NOON, THE TWINS WERE FAST asleep in the garden and still the new manager and his wife had not arrived. Trudy had just decided that they would not come till the afternoon, when she heard the familiar tooting of Tam's taxi. Rushing to the window, she saw two people alight.

Mrs. Rice was tall and her husband rather short, that was the first thing she noticed. Another quick peep revealed the fact that the lady was smartly dressed in a lime green suit with a large straw hat to match. Derek came out to shake hands with them and brought them round to the door. By this time Trudy was downstairs, ready to greet them.

"This is my wife." There was a hint of pride in Derek's voice. The lady put out an immaculately gloved hand. She would be about thirty-five, Trudy judged, with good colouring, blonde hair and greenish eyes. Her mouth was rather prim and she returned Trudy's glance by eyeing her up and down.

They shook hands and Derek said: "If you will show Mrs. Rice round the house, Trudy, I'll take Mr. Rice into the office."

"Very well, Derek. This way, Mrs. Rice."

"So you have stairs to climb," remarked the visitor in clipped tones. "Rather steep, aren't they?"

"I can't say I find them steep," was the reply.

"I can't do with stairs; they make me breathless," was the next remark.

'Oh good,' thought Trudy; 'she won't want the house,

then.' Cheerfully she proceeded with the tour of inspection. It soon became clear that the lady was determined to criticise everything she saw.

"The place is nothing but a box," she complained. "I am accustomed to a much bigger house than this."

"Well, it might be a bit cramped for a large family," Trudy admitted. "Have you got many children, Mrs. Rice?"

"Many! I have no children at all."

Trudy's hopes sank again. The house would be ample for two people. They entered the living-room with its large, bright window.

"Lovely view, isn't it?" observed Trudy.

The other shrugged. "Nice enough." Then, looking round the room, "Oh dear, what was the Bank thinking of to choose these awful shades for the walls?"

Trudy swallowed. "We—we chose them ourselves."

"Oh, I see. Well, the first thing I'd do, if I decided to take the flat, would be to change all the colour schemes. And that fireplace. What an atrocity!"

Trudy had always considered it quite a harmless sort of fireplace.

"You could change it, too, I suppose," she said weakly. "Would you like to see the kitchen now? It's through here."

The gleaming kitchen which was her pride and joy received a withering glance.

"How pokey! The one I have at present would make six of this. I don't think I could work in a place this size."

Trudy's hopes soared again. "Well, if you feel like that, Mrs. Rice—"

"And you've put up with all this for four years!"

Trudy began to bristle. "And very happy years they've been!"

Her visitor was not in the least put out.

"Of course some people are easily satisfied. I must say

I am most disappointed. James led me to believe it was an ideal home." She glared at Trudy as if it were all her fault.

"Well it has been an ideal home, to us. I'm sorry you don't like it, Mrs. Rice."

The inspection over, Trudy asked if she and her husband would care to stay for lunch. Before she had time to reply, Eva appeared at the door with a weeping twin in her arms.

"Here's Matthew," she said. "Mark woke him up and sat on top of him. He won't stop crying."

Trudy relieved her of her burden. The visitor said wonderingly, "You have two babies—twins?"

"Certainly. Matthew, pipe down! Shake hands with Mrs. Rice, there's a good boy."

Matthew held out a damp hand, which was taken very gingerly.

"I don't think we'll stay to lunch, thank you. Your hands seem to be full enough. I'll go down and find my husband. As for the house, I'll have to talk it over with him, of course."

"Just as you please, Mrs. Rice."

They went down together. Mr. Rice was waiting with Derek.

"Have you seen everything already, my dear?" he asked.

"As much as I wish to see at the moment," was the reply. "We'll have a walk round Hetherton before catching our train, James."

"You won't stay for a meal, then?" asked Derek.

Little Mr. Rice appealed to his wife. "Why not, Emily, if they'd like us to?"

You could see he was quite keen to stay, but 'Emily' gave him a look.

"No, James. Mrs. Crawford is a busy woman. She has twins to look after."

"Oh well, in that case." He looked flustered and apologetic. "I'll call again some time, Mr. Crawford, before taking over the office."

Derek said that would be all right. "And the house, Mrs. Rice, will you be taking that over, too?"

"We'll let you know about that in a day or two," was the reply.

Derek and Trudy stood looking after them.

"A nice little man," he mused. "But how did he come to marry a woman like that?"

"Probably it was she who married him. Oh, Derek, I wish you had heard her! Everything in the house was wrong. The things she said about our lovely rooms." Tears of mortification sprang to her eyes.

"Did she, indeed! Oh well, perhaps it's all for the best. But if she doesn't want it, why can't she tell us outright?"

"She's going to talk it over with her husband," Trudy informed him. "But I don't think anything he says will make any difference. She is the strong-minded one, and she let me know it!"

"Perhaps her bark is worse than her bite," suggested Derek.

"Let her bark as much as she likes, as long as she doesn't take our house from us. If she did, I'd hate her for ever."

Derek's eyebrows went up. "Hate, Trudy? I thought that was against your code."

"Well," she faltered, "so did I. But I couldn't possibly like her, could I? I don't believe you understand what this house means to me."

He put his arm round her. "Darling, it means a lot to me, too. Why shouldn't I understand?"

At that Trudy melted completely. Rubbing her cheeks against his shoulder, she murmured:

"Of course you understand. You always do. That's why I love you."

That was the cue for a loving kiss. It might have led to more, had the kettle not let out its piercing whistle. At the same moment Matthew, who had been put in his high

36

chair, yelled for attention and Mark, still in his pram, added his voice to the commotion.

"Loving will have to wait," said Trudy pulling herself away. Derek sighed. His wife was a divided person now, but he knew, none better, that like her mother she had an 'elastic heart'. The more people she loved, the more she could love.

Knowing that Esther would be anxious to hear about the visit of the Rices, Trudy got ready after lunch to go along to Two Ways, complete with pram and twins. As she turned a corner she saw Esther coming towards her, also with her family. They were beyond the pram stage now, though little Margaret still had a pramette for longer distances.

"I was coming to see you," laughed Esther.

"And I you. Great minds think alike! Well, which way is it to be?"

"Let's go for a walk," said her friend. "It's a lovely day."

They turned instinctively down the side road which led to the countryside and Broomfield. By request, Trudy Anne was allowed to wheel the twins, with their mother lending a guiding hand.

"Surely your visitors didn't stay long, Trudy?"

"They went off before lunch. Mrs. Rice just took time to find fault with everything in the flat. You'd think it was a slum, the way she spoke!"

"She had a nerve," responded Esther. "She doesn't want it, then? How relieved you must be!"

"I'm not relieved at all. It's still in the balance. She'll let us know, she says. It might be days, even weeks."

"But she wouldn't be so cruel as to keep you in suspense!"

"Wouldn't she?" was the glum reply. "I'd put nothing past a woman like that."

Esther was surprised at her vehemence. Trudy was never

quick to blame; she must have been thoroughly ruffled.

"It's not like you to say such things," she observed.

"Well, she made some very rude remarks about the things that are dear to me. However, perhaps I'm being too hasty. If we get a letter soon giving up all claim to the house, I'll forgive her."

"And so shall I," declared Esther. "Something tells me she'll not want it, Trudy, and then we'll still be neighbours. I'm just not going to consider anything else."

They walked on, two slim young women looking hardly old enough to be the mothers of their charges. Everyone who passed stopped to speak, or at least to smile to the children, for the Lawsons and the Crawfords were well known in Hetherton, chiefly owing to the good work they were doing in the mission.

At the gate of Broomfield they slowed down. As Derek had predicted, they had not seen much of Nancy since her arrival. She was either out with Roy or visiting his aunt.

"I wonder if she's there today," said Trudy. "Let's peep into the garden."

It was a garden worth peeping into. There was a large, velvety lawn and a grassy terrace with cypress trees. The borders were a mass of roses, dahlias and sweet peas, and a picturesque stream flowed through the grounds, banked by rockeries where flowers of every colour bloomed.

"It's a paradise," breathed Esther.

"And to think it may all belong to Nancy some day," Trudy reflected. "Look, Esther, there she is! On the seat beside Roy."

The pair were sitting very close together, quite oblivious to the outside world.

"Love's young dream," commented Trudy, feeling very old and wise. "We'll not disturb them, Esther."

But she had not counted on her namesake, Trudy Anne, who had no compunction about disturbing love's young dream. With a glad cry of:

"Aunt Nancy! Aunt Nancy!" she ran forward, her white socks twinkling across the lawn.

Nancy came to meet her, followed by Roy.

"Come in, everybody!" he called, and in the procession trooped.

Nancy was pleased to see them.

"That's all this garden needs, lots of wee ones to play in it. Let the twins run around, too, Trudy. They look cooped up in that pram."

Trudy was doubtful. "Are you sure Aunt Charlotte won't object to this invasion?"

Roy laughed. "Aunt Charlotte will be fast asleep. It's her rest time, my mother's, too. We'll confess later, if it worries you."

He brought them garden chairs to sit on, and spread a ground sheet for the babies to park themselves. Matthew was quite happy to sit there with some pebbles in a tin, but Mark toddled off to explore with his cousins. Roy went with them, and when they had seen enough, he gave them rides in the gardener's barrow. Squeals of merriment came to the ears of the three girls sitting on the lawn.

"Roy is in his element with children," Nancy told them. "You wouldn't expect it, with him being an only child himself and studious into the bargain, but they seem to bring out the lighter side of his nature. He's just bursting with fun, really, though he looks so solemn."

"There's a twinkle in his eye, just like Derek's," said Trudy. "Men without humour are so dreary!"

They all agreed that they were fortunate to have found partners who were by no means dreary.

"Though David sometimes keeps me too much on my toes," admitted Esther. "One never knows from day to day how he's going to jump."

Nancy agreed. "That's the artistic temperament. Remember how we used to suffer from it, Trudy? We weren't all as patient as you, Esther." She stopped to take Matthew on her lap, cuddling him to her. The little boy stroked her cheek and laughed up into her face, displaying six pearly teeth.

"Trudy, he's a pet. They're all pets, my nieces and nephews; I envy you both."

Trudy said: "Don't do that, Nancy. Your turn will come."

At this point Roy returned with Mark in his arms, the two little girls hanging on to him.

"Uncle Roy gave us fun!" exclaimed Trudy Anne happily.

"Uncle Roy a nice man," lisped Margaret. Mark had his own remarks to make.

"Down! Down!" he clamoured and staggered off again the moment he was put on the ground.

"He's a lively little chap," said Roy, looking after him. Then he smiled at Matthew, so content on Nancy's knee. "They've got different temperaments, haven't they?"

Their mother nodded. "Mark is the stronger character; he's the out-going one. I'm afraid he bullies his brother unmercifully. Someday Matthew will learn to stand up for himself, I hope."

But it was time for them to go, so the twins were bundled into the pram again, not without loud protests.

"Bring them back soon. I'd like my mother to see them," Roy said. "I'm sure she would love them."

He and Nancy came with them to the gate and waved them off.

"Well, that was very enjoyable," observed Trudy on the way back. "I just hope we weren't intruding too much on their dreams."

"They can start to dream again, now we've gone," was the reply. "Did you see his face when he looked at Nancy? I wonder what he's saying to her now!"

6

W̲HAT̲ R̲OY̲ W̲AS̲ S̲AYING̲ A̲T̲ T̲HE̲ P̲RECISE̲ moment Esther spoke was:

"Let's not go in yet, Nancy. I want to have you alone for a little."

Nancy was only too willing. The hours in each other's company were so limited. If they went off together it meant leaving Roy's mother behind and they always felt a little guilty. In Ardenlea, as well as in Broomfield, they were liable to be interrupted; it was all very frustrating to two people in love.

Roy took her to a seat in the shrubbery where they could not be seen from the house and there he put his arm round her and turned her face up to his. It was an appealing face, with its dark eyes full of love and a smile curving her lips.

"Darling Nancy," he whispered, kissing her tenderly. "I never saw anyone look so lovely as you with that baby on your knee. You love children, don't you?"

Nancy nodded emphatically. "I always have, Roy. You looked very happy yourself, amusing my nieces and nephews."

"Yes, I enjoyed it. I'm a family man at heart. Time we were married, Nancy." His voice was rueful.

Nancy in her outspoken way replied:

"Well, if you're willing, so am I!"

Roy held her hands firmly while he explained. "It's all a question of ways and means. Though Aunt Charlotte is making me her heir, at the moment I'm a comparatively poor man. The house in Hampstead is expensive to run, small though it is, and of course I've got to support my mother."

"Yes, I understand all that," murmured Nancy. "But I could keep on with my nursing, perhaps, and you and I could live in a very small way."

Roy shook his head. "When we marry, you'll be a proper wife, like Esther and Trudy. Nursing is an arduous profession. You couldn't do justice to both things."

She admitted there was some truth in his words.

"Then what are we to do?"

"We might get married and live with my mother," he suggested.

Nancy moved away from him. "No, Roy, that wouldn't do, even though your mother agreed," which she would not, was her private thought.

Roy sighed. "You do understand that I've got to look after Mother? I owe everything to her . . . She put me through college and I can't desert her now."

"Of course I understand, Roy," she assured him. "But if there's no chance of our marrying in the near future, please don't mention it at all. It just tears me in pieces and I can't stand it!"

"All right," he replied slowly. "I'll not mention it." He tried to take her in his arms again, but Nancy stiffened. She was thinking, 'If he really loved me, he wouldn't let his mother stand in the way.'

Just then they heard a footstep on the gravel, and Mrs. Melrose's voice:

"Roy! Nancy! Where are you?"

She came round the corner of the shrubbery and saw them. "Well, what are you two hiding for? Aunt Charlotte and I have had afternoon tea long ago and the tea-pot's cold."

"It doesn't matter," Roy told her. "We're not hungry, are we, Nancy?"

"Not in the least, thank you."

Mrs. Melrose sat down. "It's rather nice out here. A trifle chilly, though. Roy, will you run in and bring me a scarf, please? There's a blue one in the top drawer in my room."

He had no sooner gone than she turned to Nancy. "Well, dear, now we can have a little talk. I never seem to get you to myself at all."

Nancy said quietly: "Yes, Mrs. Melrose, what would you like to talk about?"

She laughed lightly. "It's time we got to know each other. This is a lovely place of Aunt Charlotte's, isn't it? One of the really stately homes. I suppose you know it will belong to Roy some day?"

"Oh yes, I know that."

The other patted her hand. "His wife will have a big responsibility. Do you think you could run it efficiently?"

"I could learn," said Nancy doggedly.

Another little laugh. "Of course you could. But you would be rather ignorant at first, wouldn't you?"

Nancy pulled her hand away, her quick temper flaring up.

"So you think I'm ignorant, not good enough for Roy?"

Mrs. Melrose looked shocked. "My dear, I never said such a thing! All I meant was that you would need advice. I would be very pleased to advise you."

"Thank you," choked Nancy, "but when I want advice I'll ask for it."

The minute the words were out she wished them unspoken; it had often been that way with Nancy in the past, but she thought she had conquered the failing long ago.

Her companion gave her a hurt look. "That, my dear, was a rude and unfeeling thing to say."

"I know," she replied. "I'm sorry."

But it was too late. Mrs. Melrose had risen and was walking quickly towards the house. Meeting Roy coming out with her scarf, she stopped to speak to him. Full well did Nancy know what she was saying!

Next time she looked up, Roy was there in front of her, his face pale and stern.

"Nancy, how could you?"

"How could I what?" she asked mutinously.

"Say such a thing to my mother when she was only trying to be kind."

"I didn't think she was kind," was the reply. "But I did say I was sorry."

He sat down beside her, baffled. "There are two women in my life," he said. "You and my mother. I love you both. Is it too much to ask you that you should love each other?"

Nancy's stiff lips moved. "Perhaps it is too much," she answered faintly.

Glancing at his averted face, she felt like flinging herself into his arms and promising that come what may, she would try to love his mother. But her spirit refused to unbend. They went into the house together, but, at that moment, they were poles apart.

Two days passed and still no word from the Rices.

"Surely they must guess that we are living in suspense," declared Trudy as she watched the post go by. "Of all the selfish, inconsiderate people!"

"Yes, it's hardly fair," agreed Derek. "However, I've got a feeling it will be all right."

"Esther's got that feeling, too. I wish I had! If we don't hear by tomorrow, I'm going to send Mrs. Rice a sharp letter."

Her husband grinned. "I can't see a sharp letter having any impact on that lady. She'd just send a sharper one back."

"Perhaps. I'll send a mild one, then. Or shouldn't I bother?"

44

"Wait and see," said the patient Derek.

The twins were cross that forenoon. At last Matthew consented to go for his nap in the garden, but Mark wouldn't even lie down. He stood in his cot shaking the bars and lamenting loudly, while Trudy coped with the washing machine and the cooking of lunch. She could have taken it all in her stride had her mind been at rest.

"If I only knew one way or the other," she reflected. "I really must try to cultivate patience, like Derek."

The door at the top of the stair was open so that she could hear Matthew if he cried. Instead of that she heard Nancy calling:

"Is anybody in?" She came inside, taking in at a glance the wet washing, the unpeeled potatoes and Trudy's flushed face.

"Here, I'll give you a hand." She tied on an apron and got busy with the potatoes.

"Bless you," said Trudy. "I'm tied up in knots this morning. To what do we owe the honour of this visit?"

"To the fact," replied Nancy, "that I am going back to Martonbury this afternoon."

"I thought it was tomorrow."

"Yes, but I have work to do in my hostel room, clothes to mend and so on. I must have a free day."

"I see." Trudy gave her a worried glance. "And what does Roy say about this?"

"He's relieved in a way, I think. Otherwise we'd all be going south together and he'd feel divided between me and his mother."

"Oh nonsense, Nancy."

"It's not nonsense. You know nothing about it."

It was a long time since Nancy had spoken like that. There must be a reason.

"How can I know if you don't tell me?"

"But I am telling you, Trudy. Mrs. Melrose and I don't get on and that's that."

Trudy protested—"But Nancy, it's your place to 'get on' with your future mother-in-law. She seems quite a nice person to me."

"Nice enough," was the reply, "but as I've told you before, she's got one obsession, and that's Roy. She seems to grudge every minute he spends with me. Oh, I've tried hard to be on my best behaviour, but the other day I got so angry. It was after you and Esther left us in the garden."

She threw the potatoes into the pot with such a splash that the water sparked all ways.

"Hi, be careful! You'd better tell me all about it."

Perched on a stool, Nancy went over the scene which had started the trouble.

"She was so patronising, Trudy! She inferred that I was a proper ignoramus, not fit for the position I would have as Roy's wife. She offered to give me advice and I told her when I wanted advice I'd ask for it. I was quite right, wasn't I?" she asked anxiously.

Trudy sighed. Who was she to put her sister in the right or wrong? She was so fallible herself.

"You're too hasty, Nancy; you have always been, but I thought you were getting over it."

"I thought so, too," Nancy murmured. "I said I was sorry, but Mrs. Melrose just got up and walked away. All right, I didn't mind that, but she met Roy and immediately told him what I had said. Do you call that 'nice'?"

"No, I do not," Trudy declared. "What happened then?"

"Roy was angry with me, of course. He thought it was all my fault and we nearly quarrelled. I kept my temper, but things are strained between us. Trudy, I love him so! What I felt for Godfrey Taylor was nothing to this. I believe Roy loves me just as deeply. We bring out the best in each other, except when his mother interferes."

It was a difficult problem with no obvious solution.

"So that's why I'm leaving today," Nancy went on. "But what of the future? What's to happen to us, Trudy?"

Trudy paused for reflection before replying. Then she said slowly.

"I believe things could work out, Nancy, with a lot of love. Not just love for Roy, but love for his mother, too."

Nancy gave a choked laugh. "But how can I love her when I don't even like her?"

Trudy shook her head. "I'll answer that question when I've thought more about it. Mum could give you a clue, I'm sure. Won't you confide in her?"

"No, Mum has enough worries. I've told you, because you are young and can see the situation through my eyes. Well, I'll have to be going. Must say goodbye to the twins, though. I know Matthew's in the garden, but where is Mark?"

"In his cot. He's been strangely quiet. Come and see."

They crept in to the bedroom, smiling broadly at the scene which greeted them. The cot coverings had been heaved on to the floor and Mark was fast asleep in a crouching position, his stern end sticking up comically. Feathers were everywhere; picked out of a tiny hole in his quilt.

Trudy carefully laid him straight and covered him up.

"I'll have to mend that hole quick," she whispered to Nancy as they left the room.

She was sorry to say goodbye to her sister. For Nancy the 'path of true love' seemed never to run smoothly. Compared with Esther and herself the poor girl was unfortunate indeed. You couldn't say it was any one person's fault. Nancy was to blame for her hastiness, Mrs. Melrose for her possessive attitude, and Roy for his inability to assert himself.

People! thought Trudy as she lit the gas under the potatoes. What a mix-up they were, good points and bad points battling away inside all of them. As she saw it, folk ought to be ready to sink their differences to attain their highest good. There was only one way to do that, and that was for all to believe in the same thing. If everybody believed in a good God and in His Son and carried out His teachings there would be unity, not only in families but within nations as well.

It was an ideal solution to the troubles of the world, but ideals were so hard to attain! Nothing to keep you from working towards them, however. At that moment a sizzling noise brought her back to earth. The potatoes had boiled over on to the hot stove and she made a dash to the rescue.

Derek came upstairs shortly afterwards for his meal.

"You're early," she told him. "The table isn't laid. Will you do it? I've had a busy forenoon. Nancy was here. She's leaving today, Derek. She and Roy's mother don't get on too well; isn't it a tragedy?"

"Yes, very sad." His voice sounded strange and he was looking at her in a funny way, almost timidly.

"Something's the matter. Tell me, Derek!"

He had a letter in his hand. "This came to the office with the second post. It's from the Rices."

She sat down weakly on the kitchen stool. "Is it the worst, Derek?"

"I'm afraid so. Mr. Rice says that after due consideration, unsuitable though the house is, they have decided to take it over. They will be obliged if we can let them have it by the middle of August."

She gazed at him speechlessly. When her voice came, she said:

"Let me see," and held out her hand for the letter. Yes, the words were really there, in black and white.

"Cheer up," urged her husband. "It will be all the same in a hundred years."

Cold consolation. For answer, Trudy bowed her head in her hands and began to weep stormily.

"I can't bear it," she sobbed. "I just can't bear it!"

Derek tenderly drew her hands from her face. "Sweetheart, don't take on so! I've never seen you like this before."

She gulped: "I had just begun to hope that we'd be keeping the house. You said yourself that you had a—a feeling—"

"I know. I was mistaken. Please, Trudy, stop crying! You frighten me."

His last words brought her to her senses. Here she was thinking only of herself, wallowing in self-pity. It wouldn't do. She dried her eyes on her apron and gave him a watery smile.

"I'm sorry. Forgive me, Derek." She took his lean brown hand in hers and held it to her cheek. "What am I thinking of? I've still got you and the babies and heaps of other blessings. I'll surely get over the loss of a house."

He laughed, relieved. "That's my Trudy. Now, let's have our lunch. Things never seem so bad after a meal. You will be able to eat, won't you?"

Trudy replied shakily, "I never remember not being able to eat, except when I was ill, so probably I'll be able to choke down something."

"And I," said Derek, "intend to choke down a considerable amount, so get your skates on while I lay the table."

Trudy obediently got her 'skates on', mixing sauce for the stew and dishing it out with the potatoes. It was a melancholy meal all the same.

7

WHEN THEY REACHED THE DESSERT STAGE OF the melancholy meal, which was apple pie and custard, Trudy found herself able to discuss with Derek the blow which had fallen. The worst had happened and the outcome must be faced.

"The middle of August doesn't give us very long, does it?" she mused. "I think they might have said September. However, we'll ask no favours; we'll get out. Where to, is still a mystery. Have you any suggestions?"

Derek champed up his apple pie thoughtfully. "Tomorrow's Saturday. I'm due to visit the Bank at Firton in the forenoon. The manager has left already and I've to see his deputy. The Bank house is empty, Trudy. Can you leave the babies with your mother and come and see it?"

Pause for reflection. "Well, it's always something definite to do; we can't hang fire, can we? I'll phone Mum this afternoon."

After the twins had been fed, she took up the phone and dialled the Ardenlea number. It was Ping who replied. Trudy asked:

"Is Mum there, Ping? I'd like to speak to her specially."

"Oh, indeed. Won't I do?"

"Not this time. It's important."

With an indignant snort, Ping went off to bring his mother.

"Well, Trudy?" asked Mrs. Lawson. "Have you had

news from Mr. Rice about your house?"

"Yes indeed we have, Mum. We've got to get out. They'll give us till the middle of August, that's all." If she wasn't careful those tears would start again.

Mrs. Lawson said quietly, her voice full of sympathy, "I'm so sorry, Trudy. Is there anything I can do?"

"Yes, there is, Mum. Derek wants me to go with him to look at the Bank house in Firton tomorrow morning. My mind boggles at the idea of living there, but we'll be homeless if we don't. So, if I bring the twins to you about ten o'clock, could you and Ping look after them without being too exhausted?"

"Between us we might manage," was the amused reply.

"Oh, thanks. I wish there were more people like you, Mum. What about Nancy—has she gone yet?"

"Just gone," she was informed. "She says she wants a free day before starting her duties. I'll miss her."

"Yes, we all will, but perhaps she'll get back soon. Roy, too."

She was determined to get on with things without repining. Plenty of time for that later. Regret would be sure to surge up however hard she fought against it.

Rising early next morning they scrambled through breakfast and Trudy dressed the twins in practical rompers that would take all sorts of abuse.

"We're going to Gran-gran's," she explained to them. "Gran-gran will tell you stories."

"Gran-gran got sweeties?" asked the wily Mark.

"Yes, I'm sure she has." She wished it were possible to make their hair look tidy, but it was too fine to obey the brush for more than seconds. They both had straight blond hair like silky cobwebs. It straggled down the back of their necks, making them very 'with it', but Trudy wished it would grow in curly and be less trouble.

After they were ready, she had to attend to her own toilet which in these days was a matter of secondary importance. She had a nice camel coat which covered any deficiencies, and she took a head scarf in case of rain. Her shoe supply was at a low ebb, so she wore sandals instead, thinking that if she had the heart for it, she might buy shoes in Firton.

Her mother was ready to receive her charges. Ping was there too. He said:

"Hello, Bubble!" and gave Matthew a friendly poke.

"That," Trudy informed him, "is Squeak, if you insist on giving them those awful names."

"Well, well, you could have fooled me. Perhaps I'll have learned to distinguish between them by the time you come back."

"You'll have learned a lot more than that," said Trudy darkly.

Her mother told her not to hurry back. "I'll see the twins get some nourishment. Stay in town for lunch. You and Derek will have plenty to discuss."

Trudy thanked her. "That will be a treat. At least it would be, under different circumstances!"

They had to run to catch the bus, and sat down panting. Leaving the fresh country air of Hetherton, they soon approached the industrial area with its crowded buildings, tall chimneys belching smoke, and drab surroundings. Once these places had been fresh and green, but as time went on and populations increased, the freshness was crowded out. Trudy used to worry about the same sort of thing in Martonbury when she was working in Dene's Court Mission with Derek. The Martonbury slums were now being cleared to make room for better housing, but it was taking far too long. What she longed for was a magic wand to work the transition in the twinkling of an eye.

Now they were coming into Firton. There were many fine buildings in the town, such as the group of colleges which Ping attended, but they were so crowded round by other buildings that their beauties were hidden. The main street was narrow and laden with traffic. Shops and tenements stretched on either side and there was a continuous bustle and clashing of noises that made Trudy long to hold her ears.

The bus stopped at a corner and they got off. Besides the noise, there was a heavy feeling in the atmosphere; oil fumes, smoke, and the dry smell of summer heat.

The Bank building reared up just beside them—a stone edifice stained almost black with a hundred years of city grime. The entrance to the offices was grand enough, however, and so was the manager's room which was soon to be Derek's. He took her in and introduced her to the interim manager, who gave them the key for the house above. It was with a sinking heart that Trudy laboured up the dozens of worn stone steps.

"These stairs look as if they had never been washed since the year one," she told Derek. "Not that washing them would be much good. Nothing would keep clean in this atmosphere."

At last they came to a big door which Derek opened, and they stepped inside. The air was stale and dusty and a scene of desolation met their eyes. Apparently the last tenants had gone away without bothering to tidy up. Papers and empty packets littered the floors and there was a scampering noise, like rats. Trudy hid her face against Derek's shoulder.

"Ugh! I don't want to see any more!"

He held her for a moment, his face grim. "Let's look into the rooms. They might not be so bad."

But they were. Huge barren apartments, their ceilings were high and grey and the windows so grimy it was impossible to see out. Trudy drew her finger across a window sill and withdrew it, black with soot. Impossible to keep a house like this even tolerably clean, unless you scrubbed at it night and day.

But there were other drawbacks, too. Every other minute

some huge vehicle would come thundering past in the street below, making the place shake and causing trickles of plaster to drip down from the walls. White-faced, she stared blankly at her husband.

"You know I'd live anywhere with you, Derek. But what kind of life would the twins have here?"

The same thought was in Derek's mind. Despairingly they surveyed the huge kitchen with its black fireplace and the scullery and pantry beside it. They were anything but labour saving and they could not afford much household help. Neither could they afford to carpet and decorate these huge rooms, even if the Bank offered to help.

"But we'd manage somehow. I'd even slave over the housework," declared Trudy, "if I thought it was for the babies' good. But it definitely isn't. Where would they get fresh air, peace to sleep? You can say I'm as bad as Mrs. Rice if you like, but this house is impossible."

"I thoroughly agree with you," affirmed Derek. "Come on, we'll waste no time on this relic of the past. Put it out of your mind."

Trudy felt a great relief. She had been half afraid Derek might have considered it her duty to live imprisoned in the Bank house, cut off from all her friends. But she might have known he was not that kind of husband.

Almost light-heartedly they gave up the keys and went to Denham's restaurant nearby to have their lunch. Trudy actually felt hungry, for they had had a scrappy breakfast. The menu consisted of tomato soup, roast beef and Yorkshire pudding, then trifle and ice-cream, followed by coffee.

"Gorgeous!" she declared. "Derek, we ought to do this often."

Their carefree mood took Trudy to a shoe shop where she purchased a pair of brown leather shoes for autumn. Then they boarded the return bus, Trudy still feeling as if a terrific load had been lifted from her mind. It was only when they were coming near home that a sudden drop in spirits took place. She turned to Derek, gripping his sleeve.

"It's all very well turning down the house in Firton, but where *are* we going to live?"

He shook his head gloomily. "Something may turn up. If only we had more time!"

"Yes indeed. Dear Mrs. Rice hasn't left us much of that, has she?"

They arrived at Hetherton, thoroughly deflated. Ping was at the bus stop guarding the twins in their pram. They greeted their parents with great gurgles of glee.

"Well, have they been good?" asked Trudy.

"Good, but very labour-and-time consuming. Do all babies eat up one's energies like that?"

"I only know that you were even worse than they are. Ask Mum!"

Their mother had a cup of tea ready in the big room.

"To save you asking," announced Trudy as they sat down, "we are not going to live in the Bank house," and she explained why.

"I hope you think we're right, Mum?"

Mrs. Lawson smiled. "The babies are the first consideration. This puts you in a dilemma, doesn't it?"

"I'll say!" was the inelegant reply. "Do you think we could buy a big tent or hire a caravan? We could camp out in your back garden."

Her mother looked thoughtful. "Ping and I have been discussing something, Trudy. If you don't like the idea, just speak out; but I think you ought to consider it."

"Yes, Mum? Your ideas are usually good."

"It's just this. Frankly, I am finding Ardenlea rather expensive to keep up. People like me, on a small, fixed income simply can't cope with rising rates and prices."

Trudy nodded sympathetically.

"The house is too big for Ping and myself. What about you folk coming to share it with us?"

Trudy and Derek exchanged glances. His smile was encouraging.

"But Mum, it's your house, your furniture, everything. Are you sure you'd like to share?"

"With anyone else but you, no, I wouldn't. But I think we would get on all right together, if Derek agrees. We're good friends, aren't we, Derek?"

"The best," he concurred readily.

"It's not as if you were newly married," she went on. "You have had four years to adjust yourselves. I know that two women in one house sometimes clash, especially a mother and daughter-in-law. But with a daughter such as you, Trudy, it's different. Do you follow me?"

"Yes, certainly, Mum. I'm a bit struck dumb, that's all!"

"Think of the advantages," said her mother. "It's handy here for station or bus. Derek would find it easy to travel daily."

"Yes, you would, wouldn't you, Derek? Lovely for the twins, too, and so near the village. But what does Ping think of the plan?"

"He's quite in favour. We had a long talk while the twins were having their nap. He's always had a notion to make use of the two attic rooms. One would be perfect for a study and the other for his bedroom. Some of the surplus furniture could go up there and he'd be away from noise."

"Yes, I know what noise you mean," laughed her daughter, the plan taking shape in her mind. "You mean we'd be able to bring some of our furniture? I'd hate to leave it in the flat with you-know-who."

"We'll clear out the big room for you," was the reply, "and two of the bedrooms upstairs."

"But Mum, that's too big a sacrifice!"

"Not at all. The back room downstairs is big enough for

me. I picture it as a nice, cosy bed-sitting room to which I can retire. The living-room and kitchen would be common to us all. What could be simpler?"

Trudy reflected some more. "Yes, that would leave the small bedroom for Nancy when she visits. Derek, what do you think?"

"I'll agree with whatever you say, Trudy." In fact the suggestion was a great relief to him. It would certainly give them time to look around and perhaps buy a house of their own some day.

"It's very kind of you, Mother Lawson, and of course the upkeep of the house would be our affair—rates and repairs and so on."

Trudy was still a trifle uncertain, though not on her own account. She studied her mother's face which was showing signs of approaching age, besides being thinner and paler than formerly. Or was that her imagination?

"Are you positively certain sure that you'll be able to stand being in the same house as our rumbustious twins?"

Her mother smiled. "I told you, I'll have my cosy room to retire to. But I'm looking forward to helping you. I'll be able to babysit at any time, and let you and Derek out together."

Trudy gave her a hug. "I always said you were an angel! And of course we can be of use to you, too, if ever you're ill or anything."

Mrs. Lawson said thank you very much, but she did not intend to be 'ill or anything'. "Don't make any decision tonight Trudy. Talk it over with Derek and if you change your mind, I shan't be in the least upset."

8

AT THE MORNING SERVICE NEXT DAY, THE news got around that Derek would be leaving the Bank at Hetherton. He and Trudy were beset with anxious enquiries. What was going to happen to the mission? Derek was able to reassure the enquirers.

"You're not getting rid of us as easily as that!" And he told them about their plans to stay at Ardenlea. Everybody was greatly relieved. It was their firm belief that without the Crawfords it would be impossible to carry on the good work. Trudy knew this was not so. When Derek had left Martonbury, they had had faith that the gap there would be filled and sure enough, Brian Clyde and his wife had stepped in to fill it.

Someone would have stepped in at Hetherton too, but she was thankful that the necessity had not yet arrived. By sitting up late and discussing endlessly the pros and cons, they had definitely decided to accept her mother's offer and now there was no time to lose in carrying out the removal as soon as possible. There was a great deal to arrange and many practical things to attend to.

Trudy walked back with Esther after the service. "Perhaps it's as well there is so much to be done, Esther. It will keep me from having too many nasty thoughts about that Mrs. Rice."

Esther remarked thoughtfully, "I wonder if she and her husband will take anything to do with the mission?"

"I think not; she'll be much too grand—unless I've misjudged her. I must try to keep an open mind. People are such mixtures," she reflected. "Nearly all the cranky ones have got some reason for being the way they are. They've been disappointed, or unloved, or some bitterness has eaten into them. It might be like that with Madam Rice. Someday I might find out."

"Meanwhile," Esther reminded her, "you've got plenty of other things to think about!"

It was perfectly true. Had Trudy been able to see her way clear, the task of moving house would have been heavy enough, but during the ensuing days, there were so many interruptions that she despaired of being ready for the removal date. The twins, sensing that something was in the wind, were at their naughtiest, with the result that when Derek got home to give her a hand she felt more like going to bed than renewing her efforts.

One evening he brought her a note which had been handed into the office by Mrs. Scott Brown's chauffeur.

"A peremptory summons, I expect."

"Oh dear, I ought to have gone to see her before this. She must be lonely since her visitors left, but you know how busy I've been—"

Trudy opened the note and read—"This is my 85th birthday and no one has been to see me. I need to speak to you, Trudy. Is it true you are leaving Hetherton? I think you might have told me—"

"Derek, I'll have to go tonight. The poor soul must have been moping."

"I wouldn't have said she was the type to mope, but go by all means."

"I intended to wash the curtains, too. If Mrs. Rice takes them over, they'll have to be clean."

"They look perfectly clean to me," observed her husband.

"Oh, men don't understand. Derek, did you know it was Mrs. Scott Brown's birthday? I didn't. I haven't got a present for her, unless—" her eye lit on a little blue bowl on the mantelpiece. Esther had brought it to her that afternoon, a sample of David's 'pottering'.

"I'm sure they won't mind if I give her that; I can

order another from David; he'll be glad to get a commission."

She wrapped the bowl in tissue paper and left the house with it an hour later, leaving Derek to look after the twins.

The door of Broomfield was opened by Mrs. Scott Brown's maid, Elsa, who was well known to Trudy.

"Oh, Mrs. Crawford, I'm so glad you came! The mistress has been in bed all day, too tired to get up, she says."

Trudy went up to the bedroom to find her friend lying there with an infinitely weary look on her face. She was such a vital person in spite of her great age, that Trudy had a sense of shock. She went over to kiss the wrinkled cheek.

"Thanks, Trudy! You are the only one who ever kisses me."

Trudy sat down beside the bed. "I'm sorry you don't feel so good, Mrs. Scott Brown. And I didn't know it was your birthday, or I'd have been to see you before this."

"I've had far too many birthdays," said the other ruefully. "Now, what's this about your leaving Hetherton?"

Trudy told her the truth of the matter. "We're staying on here meantime, but not at the flat. We've got to give that up. We're sharing with my mother at Ardenlea."

"Oh, you are, are you? That sort of arrangement never works out; though it might in your case, I don't know. How is your husband going to get to his job?"

"By bus, I expect."

"He ought to have a car," declared the old lady.

"Probably, but we can't afford one."

The invalid raised herself on her elbow. "Tell him to buy one and I'll foot the bill. He has looked after my money well; I owe it to him."

Smilingly, Trudy shook her head. "Thank you, but I'm afraid Derek wouldn't accept that."

"Nonsense! You're far too independent. I'll lend him the money then, how's that?"

"I'm afraid that's out too, Mrs. Scott Brown."

The other got quite annoyed. "I'll leave it to him in my will, then he can't refuse! Now, don't tell me I'm not going to die for years yet, for I know differently. It's coming very soon and I'm glad of it—do you hear that?"

Trudy patted her hand. "You're a bit down today, aren't you? Tomorrow you'll feel better."

Taking no notice, the old lady went on: "I'm not afraid of death. It's only a door opening into another room. What's through that door is bright and wonderful. Our Lord said—'In my Father's house are many mansions. I go to prepare a place for you.' I firmly believe there is a place for me, Trudy!"

The old lady had hitherto been very reticent about her beliefs, and Trudy was much moved by this declaration.

"I know there is, too," she said softly.

Mrs. Scott Brown lay back on her pillows. "So, please, when the time comes, don't have any regrets for me. I've had a long life, longer than I deserved." She gave her characteristic chuckle. "Eighty-five! To think I was a weakly child. They said I wouldn't make 'old bones'. Well, I've cheated them all!"

"To be sure, you have." Trudy took the blue bowl from its wrapping. "This is just a small gift for your birthday."

The invalid took it in her thin old hands. "Very pretty. I like the colour. But you did not need to bring me anything."

"It's a sample of my brother's work," Trudy informed her, and went on to talk about David's new hobby.

"The trouble is, a bungalow isn't exactly suitable for such an occupation."

"I should think not. Tell your brother to come and see me. I am interested in young folk like him, with a creative urge. We need creative people in this world of automation; it's a soul-killing process. You'll have to work very hard, you and your friends, to keep people's souls alive in the days to come."

It was a timely prophecy which reinforced Trudy's own convictions.

"You may rely on us to do our best," she promised.

One day, when everything was in a state of upheaval, Trudy went to answer the telephone. The voice was Mrs. Rice's and her clipped tones ruffled her at once.

"I hope it will be convenient for me to come today to take some measurements?" she asked.

It certainly was not convenient, but Trudy gave in to save argument.

"After lunch, then, Mrs. Rice. The curtains are still up if you wish to buy them."

"I'll have a good look at them first," was the reply.

Trudy felt it would take her all her time to be civil. But she had told Esther she would look for the visitor's good points and made up her mind to do so. Ping, who was still at home, took the twins for an outing, which was very obliging of him, as he was at an age when young men are very sensitive about being seen pushing a pram.

When Mrs. Rice arrived, Trudy greeted her with a smile, which was returned very fleetingly.

"The house is even smaller than I thought," was the first remark. "However, it will have to do, I suppose!" She got out her inch-tape to measure the floors.

"As I thought, I shall have to get rid of some of my furniture. It's such good stuff, too!" Her tone made Trudy feel guilty.

"And the curtains?" she asked.

The visitor went round fingering the materials and studying the colours of the hangings Trudy had selected so carefully. When she came to the kitchen and saw the curtains with the seagulls, she laughed cuttingly.

"Well, I shan't be requiring these, anyway. I couldn't live a day with those seagulls!"

Trudy flushed. "I have managed to live with them for four years. I like seagulls."

"There's no accounting for tastes," was the dry response.

She decided to keep the other curtains, however. "They're not what I would have chosen myself and of course they're not new. But they might do me till I get more suitable ones. How much do you want for them?"

Trudy mentioned a sum which she thought fair. The lady scoffed.

"Mrs. Crawford, you have no idea of values. I could get them new for that."

It wasn't true, of course. "What would you agree to pay, then?"

Mrs. Rice offered half of the original sum. "That's all they're worth to me. Of course, you don't need to take it, if you'd rather keep the things."

But what use would the curtains be at Ardenlea where the windows were so much bigger? Bargaining was a thing Trudy hated; in fact she was totally inexperienced, so she gave in. But all her dislike of the woman came rushing up again. She had to fight hard to say politely:

"Would you like to look at the garden now?"

Mrs. Rice agreed, and proceeded with her critical inspection. She seemed blind to the glory of the roses and the rainbow lupins, but made remarks about the lack of gravel on the paths and the absence of fruit bushes.

"That's quite a nice garden seat, though," she condescended to remark.

"Yes," Trudy told her. "It's a wedding anniversary present from my husband."

She was glad when the ordeal was over. The more she saw of Mrs. Rice the less she liked her. When she came here to live it might be best to avoid her completely. "Yes," thought Trudy, "that's what I'll do. Otherwise this hate-thing will get the better of me altogether."

The 'flitting' day came at last. The carpets from the flat had already been laid at Ardenlea, some furniture had been sold and the rest was waiting to be transported.

Derek had the day off and after an early breakfast Trudy took the twins round to Esther's, so that they would be out of the way. When she returned, the removal van was at the door. Not till this moment did she actually realise that this, the home to which she had come as a bride, was now her home no longer.

The men with the van were a merry group and manoeuvred the furniture down the narrow staircase, joking all the way. Trudy stood at the top watching the things disappearing one by one, till there was nothing left but small articles like brushes and pails and kitchen utensils. Then they were taken, too, the van doors were shut and the loaded vehicle began to lumber downhill. Derek had gone too, and Trudy was left alone watching from the window.

When there was nothing more to see, she turned to survey the empty lounge which had been her main delight, then wandered round the house recalling the years she had spent there. No other house would ever mean so much to her. Within these walls she had spent her happiest moments and thought her deepest thoughts. Here she had learned the meaning of wifehood and motherhood, learned how to love and how to make sacrifices. Surely some of all that would linger after she had gone?

Having put the place straight, Trudy said a last good-bye to the rooms. The kitchen was the last. It was stripped except for the seagull curtains. By rights they ought to be thrown out, but when she got downstairs she found she hadn't the heart to dispose of them. Old and all as they were, they would go with her.

At the foot of the stairs she met Eva with a letter in her hand.

"Well, Eva! Have you been getting good news?"

The girl hesitated. "Not exactly. It's a letter from my mother. She has changed her mind about 'washing her hands' of me, Trudy. She and my stepfather are setting up house in London. They've invited me to share it with them. She has promised me everything I could wish for, on one condition."

"Yes?" said Trudy—"and what's that?"

"You can guess. That I give up my friends here. You know I couldn't do that, Trudy!"

"No," said Trudy slowly, "I don't believe you could. Is this your last chance, then?"

"Positively, she says. But I don't care, I'm not going! You do agree with me, Trudy?"

"Of course I do. But you must give it careful thought, Eva. I know it didn't work last time, but this time might be different."

Eva shook her head. "This is the place and you are the people that I love best on earth. But I shouldn't be talking about myself when here you are, saying goodbye to your lovely little house. Are you quite finished up there, Trudy?"

"Quite finished. Here are the keys, Eva. I'll leave them with you."

Eva looked at the keys in her hand regretfully. "I'll miss Derek and I'll miss you more than I can say."

"But we'll not be far away. Besides, you're going on holiday in a day or two."

Her face brightened. "Yes, I'm looking forward to that."

And to being with Ping, thought Trudy, smiling maternally. Then she took up her basket, full of odds and ends, and prepared to depart. There must be no regrets, she told herself firmly. To brood on the past was a mistake; one must live in the present and look towards the future, it was the only hopeful thing to do.

9

Having made up her mind to make the best of her new circumstances, Trudy found that things promised to work out quite well. She and her mother had such close understanding that there was seldom cause to differ, and Derek had no call to 'take sides', as so often happens when families live together.

True, the twins might have been a bone of contention, for everybody has their own ideas on the bringing-up of children, but Mrs. Lawson wisely left all that in the hands of her daughter, not giving advice unless it was asked for. Trudy on her part worked in with her mother's methods of housekeeping, which did not differ greatly from her own.

It was all a question of goodwill. Without goodwill, nothing would go right either at home or in the larger affairs of the outside world. Why wouldn't people realise that and stop all those quarrels which brought ruin and misery to so many?

A few days after they settled in, Ping and Eva went off to help with the seaside mission at Carencross. Trudy and her mother went to the station to see them off. The twins were there too, of course. Trains were a great attraction to them and now they were much nearer the railway than before.

Eva was looking very dainty in a white coat over a summer frock, and Ping very manly and protective. They leaned out of the carriage window to wave goodbye and as the train faded from view, Trudy turned to her mother:

"How young they are! Especially Eva. Young and trusting. I do hope she is never disillusioned. She has a very sensitive nature, easily hurt."

66

Her mother agreed. "Yes, she feels things twice as much as other people. A pity, for she is bound to get knocks. Nobody escapes them!"

"Mum," Trudy observed as they walked away, "Eva has had another offer from her mother to go to London, but she says she's not going. I think I know the chief reason. She's in love with Ping. Do you think he loves her, too?"

The other smiled. "It looks very like it."

"Then why don't they get engaged and make sure of each other?"

"As to that," was the reply, "you must consider Ping's position. Eva's people are wealthy; he is only a 'poor student'. I'm sure he would not tie Eva down till he had something to offer her."

"Then he's wrong. She's so pretty and appealing, some other man might snatch her from him!"

"Or some other girl might snatch Ping from Eva," suggested her mother. "They'll have to work it out for themselves, Trudy."

"I suppose so," agreed her daughter. "But wouldn't it be thrilling if they did come back engaged!"

Meanwhile the train was bearing the young couple towards Carencross, a favourite holiday place with a sandy bay which was perfect for holding meetings for young people and children.

Though Eva looked so demure and calm, she was inwardly excited at the prospect of being alone with Ping, and seeing him every day for a whole fortnight. She had forgotten about the other claims on his time, had overlooked the fact that there would be other people there too, friends of his whom she did not know.

They were there to meet him at the station, a group of youths and girls of his own age. Overcome by shyness, Eva was very quiet when introduced and kept in the background, half wishing she had not come.

Ping turned to her. "Eva, here is somebody who will tell you all about our activities. Doris, meet Eva."

The girl beside him was tall and dark with long-lashed brown eyes and a competent air. She took Eva's arm.

"Come with me and I'll show you where we're staying. The men camp out, but we girls have a house to ourselves. You've to share a room with me."

From that moment, Ping was swept out of Eva's sight. Doris took her along the promenade and up a narrow lane to a grey stone villa.

"It's a bit shabby, but it's cheap, which is the main consideration," said the girl as they went upstairs. "This is our room. We have a meal at six, which gives us time for a chat."

She sat down on the bed and Eva took a chair.

"Tell me about the mission, please. Do you work very hard?"

"Hard enough!" declared Doris. "We have children's meetings in the forenoons. Sing-songs and games and Bible Quizzes and things like that. In the afternoons we run picnics or go off on our own. Evenings are mainly for teenagers. If it's cold or wet we have a hall for them and run a café. But if it's dry we sometimes have a 'sausage sizzle' on the beach."

Eva laughed. "It sounds very entertaining. Don't you have anything more serious?"

"Yes, of course. There's a certain amount of religious teaching, but if it was all that, nobody would come—see? Ping's rather keen on the teaching side, but then, he can make it interesting. He holds them in the palm of his hand. We've missed him very much lately."

Eva was thoughtful. "You call him 'Ping!' I thought you'd know him as 'Peter'."

"Sure," said the other, "but I wormed his pet name out of him. We're students together, you know, at Firton
68

college. I'm doing Philosophy."

It sounded very grand to Eva. This girl Doris must be very clever indeed.

"It must be nice to have brains," she said with a little sigh. Nice to be brilliant enough to keep up with Ping, she meant. Up till now it hadn't worried her, but she began to wonder—was she really worthy to be a friend of his, let alone the something closer that she had dreamed of in her heart?

The doubt grew stronger as the days went by. Among the young folk who were running the mission, Ping was the most popular, the most sought after. He seemed to have no time for old friends, pondered Eva, greatly hurt. When she did get a chance to speak to him, Doris nearly always happened to turn up to draw attention to herself. Had she been less shy, Eva would have put herself forward, but such was her nature that the more Ping seemed to ignore her, the more she drew into the background.

One morning she woke very early to find Doris sitting up in bed with a large book on Philosophy in front of her.

"Studying already?" Eva enquired.

"My brain's always clearer in the mornings," was the explanation. "Though I must say this is heavy going. What do you make of it?"

She read a sentence or two aloud, but Eva had to admit she made nothing of it; it was far beyond her understanding.

"I suppose Ping would understand it," she commented.

"Oh, it's simple to Ping! He always helps me with the difficult bits."

That did it. Eva felt a stab as she pictured Doris and Ping, their heads together, discussing the inner meaning of the difficult sentences. She threw off the bedclothes and leapt out of bed. The room seemed to be stifling her.

"It's far too early to get up!" remonstrated Doris.

"Not at all. It's a lovely morning. I'm going out."

"Please yourself," was the short reply.

Having dressed, Eva went downstairs where she seemed to be the only one on the move. Going out into the stillness of the morning, she walked down the lane to the beach. The sea shone before her, smooth as glass, and there on the turf the campers' tents made a colourful show. At first nothing moved, then she saw a figure emerging from one of the tents and her heart gave a bound. It was Ping.

She ran forward to greet him.

"Why, Eva, you're up early!"

"I couldn't sleep," she told him.

"Oh, I'm sorry about that. I slept like a log myself. What is the matter, Eva? Aren't you enjoying it here?"

She said stoutly, "Of course I am! I'm a bit shy of everyone, that's all."

"But there's no need to be shy, they're all friends. You're getting on all right with Doris, aren't you?"

Eva said "Of course," to that, too, adding, "She's very clever, isn't she?"

"One of the best in every way," declared Ping. "I wish I had more time to show you round, Eva, but you can see how things are. Some day I must take you to see the old castle; it's a picture."

"Will you really? You couldn't take me today, Ping?" she asked anxiously.

He shook his head. "No chance, I'm afraid. They're depending on me to take the forenoon meeting and we're hiring rowing boats for a picnic later on."

"There's always the evening," she put in.

"Don't you remember? We've invited the parents to the hall tonight. I simply must be there."

"Oh well," she did her best to sound bright, "it's all right, Ping, don't worry about me."

Ping's pals came out of their tents just then and

immediately he was in demand, so Eva went back to the house to help with breakfast. There were plenty of jobs to do, inside and out. When the time came for the meeting on the beach she did her part, too, looking after the smaller children who were always straying away.

On so fine a day they gathered a large crowd, for mothers were always pleased to be relieved of their duties for a short time. They knew their youngsters would be safe with these earnest young people and though many of them were without religion themselves, they thought it would be good for their children; which to Eva's mind was a very twisted way of looking at things.

As for Ping and his friends, they loved to see the small, bright faces turned to them and to hear the eager voices join in the choruses. Though not expecting dramatic results, they were convinced that some of the good seed which they scattered would fall on fertile soil.

The sail in the afternoon would have been enjoyable, except for the fact that Ping and Eva were on different boats and she hardly saw him at all. Doris never left his side, however. They did everything together and seemed the best of friends. Eva's spirits sank lower still when she happened to hear two of the girls discussing the pair.

"I smell romance," laughed one. "What price an engagement soon?"

"Peter and Doris?" said the other. "I shouldn't be surprised. They've certainly got plenty in common. They'd go places together."

Eva moved away, her face burning. The holiday to which she had looked forward so much was all spoiled. Ping did not want her; nobody wanted her; she should never have come.

In the evening she made an excuse not to attend the meeting. She had a headache, she said, and she really did have one. But she was too restless to stay indoors and soon wandered out alone along the bay to where there were no houses, just trees, grass, rocks and utter silence.

A narrow road turned up from the shore and a sign said 'To Castle Doran'. This must be the beauty spot Ping had told her about. Instinctively she followed the road past a row of picturesque cottages to a grassy mound on which rose the ruins of a fine old castle overgrown with ivy and creepers.

There was something so forlorn about it that tears sprang to Eva's eyes. The world was a very sad place, she thought, especially if the person you loved was in love with someone else. Common sense ought to have told her before this that Ping was bound to come in contact with girls more attractive than herself, girls who were fit to 'go places' with him, like Doris who studied Philosophy.

She wiped her eyes, calling herself a silly little fool, not that it made her feel any better. Then she turned away from the sight of the ruins and made to retrace her steps, but at that moment two figures came in to view walking in her direction. She took one look then raced back along the narrow road as if someone were chasing her. For the two people were Ping and Doris.

As she ran she felt her heart contract with misery. So Ping had brought Doris here instead of bringing her. Had these two left the meeting early or had they not been there at all?

"I'll never speak to him again," sobbed Eva. "Never! Never!"

At last, out of breath, she was obliged to stop. The road had narrowed to a mere track and she had lost even that. She was in the middle of nowhere and it was getting dark. Cold, too. The sooner she got back to the house the better.

It took her a long time to find the road again and when at last she arrived back she was weary beyond words.

Doris was still awake. "What's wrong? Where have you been?" she demanded.

"I went for a walk and got lost," Eva managed to get

out, but she said no more. Through the night she lay awake, making her plans. She could not possibly stay here any longer. To see Ping every day knowing that he did not care for her would be sheer torture. She was a misfit here, anyway; no doubt he would get on better without her. But where would she go? Not back to Hetherton, for everything there would remind her of him.

That letter from her mother with its invitation to join her in London was still unanswered. She would set off for the capital early in the morning. If she was going to be miserable, she might as well be miserable there as anywhere else.

Had her tension been eased by a good sleep, Eva might have thought again about taking such a step, but she was so dazed with lying awake all night that she had no sensible thoughts left, except to leave a note for Ping.

"Dear Ping," she wrote, "I don't know what you will think of me, but I have decided to go to London to my mother. I'm sorry to be deserting the work here, but I don't think I'm much good at it and you have plenty of helpers without me. Later on, I'll write to the folk in Hetherton and explain. I guess my mother will be pleased to see me." Her pen would write no more except the one word —"Goodbye."

Then, leaving the sealed envelope addressed to 'Mr. Peter Lawson' on the hall table, she slipped out of the house with her suitcase. Only the girls on kitchen duty were awake, but they did not hear her leave.

Making her way to the railway station she decided to take the first train that came in, whatever its destination. From there she would get a connection for London. Her mother had sent her money, so there was no difficulty there. That she was doing something that would hurt a great many people Eva did not consider at the moment. She was a young girl in love and her feelings had been so wounded she was hardly accountable for her actions.

10

Now THAT THEY WERE SETTLED IN Ardenlea, Trudy did her shopping in the village and found things very pleasant there. But there were occasions when she was obliged to take the road up the hill and pass the Bank house where she had been so happy. When doing so she always turned her head the other way, for the loss of her home still hurt. Besides, she did not wish to catch sight of Mrs. Rice if she could help it. She could not remember any single person who had been able to rouse such angry feelings in her, so it was best to forget her as far as possible.

That was why, as she pushed the twins' pram up towards Two Ways one sunny forenoon to visit Esther, she kept to the other side of the road, gazing straight ahead.

But Mrs. Rice had seen her. She came out of the house and crossed over, followed by a little barking dog which immediately snapped at Trudy's heels.

"Quiet, Jackie!" But it was only a half-hearted command, and during their conversation Jackie continued to bark and snap.

"You wished to speak to me, Mrs. Rice?" asked Trudy.

"It's about that garden seat," was the reply.

"The garden seat—what do you mean?"

"You must know, Mrs. Lawson. It was there in the garden when I came to view the house. Now it has gone."

"Of course it has," declared Trudy. "We took it with us. It was a present from my husband on our first wedding anniversary."

"I'm afraid that does not affect me," said the other. "You had no right to remove that seat. It was there when you showed me round and it ought to have remained there."

"Not at all," protested Trudy. "We left you the plants and bushes because they were growing in the garden. But the seat wasn't growing. It's furniture."

The lady reddened. "It was part of the garden. I'll be obliged if you will return it immediately. Otherwise, I'll have to take steps—"

Though indignant, Trudy kept her voice steady. "Nothing you can say or do will make me return that seat, Mrs. Rice. Please understand that."

In a spiteful voice, the other replied: "Very well. But I shan't let the matter rest there, you may depend on it!"

The twins had been regarding the stranger with big, anxious eyes. Now, what with the angry tones and the barking of the dog, the sensitive Matthew could bear it no longer. He put on what his Gran called a 'petted lip' and burst into tears. Mark immediately joined him and Trudy was left to calm down the duet, while Mrs. Rice, with a disgusted snort, marched away with the yapping Jackie at her heels.

"Imagine," Trudy confided in Esther while they drank their 'elevenses', "she actually thought I'd hand over my beloved seat at her bidding. I'm still angry at how she cheated me about the curtains, but this is unforgivable!"

Esther gave her a puzzled look from her calm blue eyes.

"I never thought to hear that word from you, Trudy. 'Unforgivable'."

Trudy felt ashamed. "I ought not to have said it. But that woman rouses the worst in me. Yet we're told to love our enemies. How is it possible?"

"You used to think it was possible," was the thoughtful reply. "Remember Katrina Swan at college and all these other people you managed to win over in the end?"

"Yes, but I've never come across anyone like Mrs. Rice.

Or perhaps it's just that I'm slipping. Can it be that I'm not fit to practise what I preach?"

"Of course you are. You're being tested, that's all," said her friend.

Trudy considered. "Tested? Perhaps you're right. But how can one help feeling indignant sometimes? You can't drown every feeling; it wouldn't be natural. Just think, we'd all be robots."

Esther chuckled. "What a fate! No, Trudy, I think feelings are necessary, even angry ones. But to be unforgiving is different, again. That's lack of feeling. Drink up your coffee before it gets cold."

Trudy did so. Esther spoke the truth; she must try harder to feel more kindly towards the woman who had dispossessed her.

Esther changed the subject. "Have you had any word from Eva since she went to join Ping?"

"Just a postcard; she didn't say much. Nothing from Ping; he's a bad correspondent at the best of times. But I hope they'll have news when they come home."

Esther smiled. "I can guess what kind of news you mean."

But if they had known what was taking place at that moment, they would not have been so hopeful.

The telephone rang at lunch time while Trudy was telling her mother about the encounter with Mrs. Rice. She broke off to go and answer it, thinking it might be from Derek in his new post at Firton. But the voice she heard was Ping's.

"Trudy, something awful has happened. Eva has gone away!"

"Gone away?" she asked, puzzled. "Where to, Ping?"

"To her mother in London. She left a note."

"I don't understand. Eva definitely told me she was not going to London. Something must have happened at Carencross. Wasn't she happy there?"

"As to that," Ping said slowly, "I couldn't be sure. I really haven't seen much of her, I've been too busy. Why has she done this to me, Trudy?"

"You should know that better than I," was the sisterly response. "But if you want her back you'd better go after her, hadn't you?"

"Yes," said Ping, "and that's why I phoned. She gives no address in her note. Do you know where her mother lives?"

Trudy pondered. "I've no idea where their new home is, but perhaps they're not in it yet. When I visited Eva in London that time, they were staying in a hotel near Hyde Park. Perhaps you might find her there." She gave him the name of the hotel and directions how to find it. "It's just a chance, though."

"A chance I must take," declared Ping. "This has been a blow, Trudy! If Eva's never coming back, nothing is worth while to me. Do you understand?"

"Of course I do. You must find her, Ping. Something must have made her feel very insecure. She's a tender plant, our Eva."

"Don't I know it! Thank you, Trudy. I'll let you know how I get on."

Trudy went back to her mother to report the conversation.

"Now, whatever made Eva do such a thing! I know for a fact that she was all against going to London. It looks as if Ping had neglected her a little and she went off in a pique. I'm disappointed in Eva. Ping deserves better treatment."

"I agree it was a thoughtless thing to do," observed her mother. "But we don't know the whole of it. There may have been a misunderstanding. If so, it can be cleared up, provided he finds her before it's too late."

At this juncture, Matthew spilled his milk over the carpet and there was a rush to mop it up. The problem of Eva was set aside for the moment, but it came back in full force to occupy Trudy's mind for the rest of the day. How would Ping fare in his search, and would they be able to patch up their quarrel, if such it was?

When Ping had got Eva's note and realised that she had gone, perhaps never to come back, his mind began to whirl. Why? Why? He asked himself. Then he began to think things over. Eva had come to help with the work here to oblige him, but surely she realised that he would be too busy to pay her individual attention? He had handed her over to the care of Doris Lambert, a capable girl if ever there was one. Doris was always there when things needed to be done; she had become almost indispensable, that was why they were together such a lot. Perhaps Eva had noticed and taken the wrong meaning out of it. But she couldn't actually believe that he and Doris—? Surely Eva knew that she was the one girl for him? Yet she had written—"You have plenty of helpers without me". She must have felt unwanted. Eva—unwanted!

Another thought troubled him. He recalled what had happened last night at the end of the meeting, when word was brought to him that a young boy, one of those who had been attending the mission, had met with an accident. He had set off to visit the lad, who lived in one of the cottages near the castle, and Doris had offered to accompany him. Turning into the castle road, he caught sight of a figure which looked very like Eva. It was dusk, however, and in another minute the figure had disappeared. But had it been Eva? If so, she must have seen them and drawn her own conclusions.

What was worse, reflected Ping, was the fact that when Eva asked him to take her to the castle that night, he had put her off. Had she actually thought he had a prior date with Doris? No wonder she had been hurt. It would all have to be cleared up; he would not rest until he found her and explained. Even the importance of his mission work paled for the moment.

After making the necessary arrangements, Ping set off for the railway station. Doris insisted on seeing him off. She was all against his going.

"You're needed here, Ping. If Eva doesn't like it, why force her to come back?"

"I just want to know what's happened to her," he explained.

"Why?" asked the girl pertly. "Surely a dumb little creature like that doesn't mean anything to you?"

Ping went white. "You have entirely the wrong impression about Eva. As a matter of fact, she means everything to me."

It was Doris's turn to grow pale. "If I had known that, Peter Lawson, I'd never have come to your old mission!"

Her confession was a shock to Ping. So absorbed was he in the good work for its own sake, he had imagined all his helpers had the same high motives.

"You mean, Doris, you don't really believe in the message we're trying to get across?"

Her lip curled. "Oh, I believe there is something in what you preach, but I'm not really interested, except in so far as it concerns yourself. It's you I'm interested in," and she gave him a rather bold smile which made Ping blush to the roots of his hair.

"Well," he said, "I'm sorry, but your interest is not returned. I like and admire you, Doris—at least I did till you made that admission just now. To pretend to a belief which one does not hold is worse than not believing at all."

Doris merely laughed. "Oh, Ping, you're too high-souled for words! Some day you'll have to come down a peg."

"I hope and pray not," murmured Ping. Then the train came in.

There was a good connection for London and he arrived there in the evening, still feeling the strain. He waited at a bus stop, utterly bewildered by his surroundings, for unlike Trudy he had never visited the capital before. In normal circumstances he would have thoroughly enjoyed the experience, but his only desire today was that among all those thronging multitudes he might catch a glimpse of the face that meant all the world to him.

Small chance of that among so many! These were strangers all intent on their own affairs. Yet weren't they all members of the same human family, in the care of the same loving Father?

At last he spotted the bus he required. It deposited him at the splendid portico of the hotel, but he had to pause awhile before plucking up courage to go inside. Though quite used to addressing audiences and to speak up boldly about the things he believed in, Ping had never acquired the polish and sophistication of the city dweller. He knew little about hotels and the haunts of the wealthy and felt decidedly awkward in their midst. Beside, the clothes he wore were more suitable to the seaside than his present surroundings!

However, he could not go through life letting shyness get the better of him. He took a bold step through the revolving doors and after some indecision approached the reception desk.

"Excuse me, but can you tell me if a Miss Somers has booked in here today?"

The clerk looked him up and down, then seemed to decide he was quite respectable. He consulted his books.

"Sorry, sir, there does not seem to be anybody of that name."

Despondently Ping was leaving the hotel when it suddenly struck him that Eva might have used her mother's name which was now—what was it? If he could only remember! He stood on the step outside searching his memory. Something beginning with 'W'. He had it! Woodrow. He went back to the desk and made further enquiries. In vain. Neither Eva nor her mother and step-father were booked in here.

Now, what to do? He had simply no clue about how to find Eva among those teeming millions. He doubted if the police could help even if he asked them, and what right had he to do that? He walked slowly away, then, not knowing which way to turn, he stood gazing at a book-shop window reading the titles of the books, but not tak-ing them in. Should he go right back to Carencross or stay here and keep on looking? But he might stay for weeks and months and still never find her.

Once before, Eva had gone out of his life and every-thing had lost its savour. Her return had made all the difference, but he had been so busy with his studies and other affairs that perhaps he had taken her for granted. He blamed himself, now that it was too late.

"If only," he told himself miserably, "I could see her now, I'd make up for all that!"

Then, just as his spirits had reached their lowest ebb, he felt a gentle hand on his elbow. He turned sharply and there was Eva beside him, her sweet, tear-stained face turned up to his.

"Ping, oh Ping, where did you come from?" she stam-mered.

He seized her hands, joy consuming him. "I came to look for you, of course!"

For a few moments nothing more was said. They just stood there gazing at each other.

"Eva, you've been crying," were Ping's next words.

"I know." Her lip trembled. "I've been a silly little donkey, Ping. Are you very angry with me?"

"Yes, I am," was the straight response. "Didn't you know how upset I'd be? But we can't talk here. Let's find a better place."

They walked on, hand in hand, till they came to a snack bar with chairs and tables. He took her inside and they sat down. Going to the counter, he came back with a tray of tea and buns.

"There, you'll feel better after some food. Take your time and tell me everything."

She took a bite or two, surveying him with misty eyes.

"Oh Ping, it is good to see you! I didn't know what to do. The minute I got off the train I knew I had made a terrible mistake. Last time I lived in London I came to hate it and I know I'd hate it again."

Ping said dryly, "A pity you didn't realise that before you got on the train at all."

"I know." She blinked away tears. "Will you ever forgive me?"

"I'll think about it," he said, smiling. "You haven't seen your mother, then?"

"No. You remember her conditions? If I went to her, I'd have to give up my friends in Hetherton. Not only that, I'd have to take up her way of life. She doesn't believe what we believe, Ping. She doesn't believe in anything. I might come to be like that, too. I nearly did before."

Ping nodded. "I understand, Eva. What have you being doing with yourself, then?"

"I don't quite know. Wandering around trying to make up my mind. Then I remembered about this hotel where I stayed before and was going to book in for the night. I had to stay somewhere!"

"Exactly," said Ping. "A good thing you did come this way or I'd never have found you. Trudy gave me the name of the hotel but I drew a blank there. Still, all's well that ends well."

"Yes, I suppose so." She looked at him shyly across the table. "I can't face going back to Carencross, Ping. Is that cowardly?"

"Not really. You can go back to Hetherton."

"But the Coopers are on holiday. The house is closed."

"Then you can stay at Ardenlea. They'll be delighted to see you."

Ping pushed back his cup and saucer, put his arms on the table and looked straight into her eyes.

"I've got to know something, Eva. What was your real reason for running away?"

Her eyes fell, the long lashes lying mutely on her cheeks. In a thin little voice she replied:

"I'd rather you did not ask me that."

"But I am asking it and I deserve a reply. In fact, I demand one." His tone was masterful.

A quick glance from her very blue eyes, then in a rush she whispered:

"Because—because I thought you liked Doris better than me."

So he had guessed correctly. He seized her hand and held it tight.

"I like nobody better than you. Remember that."

"But," she faltered, "Doris is so clever. I don't know anything, Ping. I'm just an ignoramus. And I do such silly things!"

Ping laughed. "You are you. Do you think I want you any different? As for Doris, she's just a bit too clever. You saw us on the castle road last night, then? I can explain about that—" and he went on to do so. It made Eva feel very happy; her eyes began to shine.

"That's more like it," said Ping. "Now, eat up your bun and get that room booked. You'd better get some beauty sleep before we go back."

"And what are you going to do?" she asked.

"Oh, I'll find more humble quarters. I'll call for you in the morning and we'll get an early train. Right?"

"Right," said Eva joyously.

11

As Ping had foretold, Trudy and her mother welcomed Eva gladly. What was more, they asked no questions, knowing that the story was bound to come out someday. Anxious to show her gratitude, Eva gave a helping hand and was a great favourite with the twins. Trudy was glad to have her, for her mother was ailing. It was only the warm weather, she said; after a rest she would be as fit as ever, but still it was a worry.

Passing the Bank house one day on her way to Esther's, Trudy took a quick glance at the windows. Good, there was no one there, no sign of life. Relieved, she was passing on, when Mrs. Rice suddenly appeared on the road, blocking the way. The little dog was there too, giving menacing little barks.

"That matter I spoke to you about, Mrs. Crawford. I am still waiting!"

All the 'hate-feeling' Trudy had been trying to stifle surged up again. She replied coldly:

"If you are referring to the garden seat, Mrs. Rice, I'm afraid you'll go on waiting."

The lady went pink. "I said I would take steps and I intend to do so! That seat is mine by rights."

"Not at all," was the reply. "My husband knows the law and he says you have no claim on it."

"Indeed! Then your husband is wrong. I'll be sending for the seat in a few days. You had better give it up gracefully."

Trudy's chin went up. "I don't intend to give it up." Then, softening, she laid a hand on her arm:

"Please, Mrs. Rice, let us be friends. Why should we bicker like this?"

It was no use. "You know what to do if you want to be friends. Otherwise, it's out of the question."

Trudy went on with the pram, thinking how hopeless it was. As usual, she opened her heart to Esther.

"She hasn't a leg to stand on and she knows it, Esther. Send for the seat indeed! She wouldn't have the nerve."

Esther, handing out biscuits to the four children, replied, "Poor thing, she sounds a thoroughly unhappy woman. There must be a reason."

"I suppose so, but don't let's waste time discussing her."

The children were despatched to the garden and the two mothers kept an eye on them while they talked. Esther asked about Eva.

"Is she still with you?"

"Yes, but the Coopers are home now, and she's going back there tomorrow. We'll miss her. She's been very helpful."

"Did you ever find out what went wrong at Carencross?" asked her friend.

Trudy shook her head. "No, and I don't like to ask her. I think she's a bit ashamed of having run away."

"Is the romance still going strong?"

"As far as I know. Ping seemed very protective when he brought her back, but still no word of an engagement. They're young, of course."

"Couples get married very young these days," commented Esther in grandmotherly fashion. "But I guess Nancy will be first. Her prospects are good, aren't they?"

"More or less. When Roy inherits Broomfield they'll be rich, but that might not be for a long time."

Esther said seriously, "I'm not so sure, Trudy. David was there last night. You told him Mrs. Scott Brown wanted to see him, remember? I had a job persuading him to go, but when he got there he was told the doctor was in, and the old lady had taken a turn for the worse."

It was disturbing news. "Poor Mrs. Scott Brown. Not that she isn't prepared, Esther. She is a devout person; her faith is strong," and she told her friend something of their last conversation. The two then sat in thoughtful silence till a commotion outside brought them to their feet. Esther's two little girls were staggering round each burdened with a twin, but Mark's weight had finally been too much for Margaret and the two of them had fallen over and were letting out cries of woe. By the time peace had been restored, faces washed and sweets distributed, it was time for Trudy to depart.

"It's your turn to come and see me next, Esther! Come on Tuesday if that suits."

But before Tuesday came they got the sad news that Mrs. Scott Brown had died. She had told Trudy she was not afraid of death and there were to be no regrets, but Trudy could not help feeling sorrowful. She was going to miss the 'old warrior', as the people of Hetherton called her. Most of them were unaware that the old lady had a soft heart beneath that grim exterior; but some of the mission folk had known her softer side, and sincerely mourned her passing.

Roy and his mother came north for the funeral. The day after his aunt was laid to rest in the peaceful cemetery beside the village church, the young man paid a visit to Ardenlea. In the big front room there he held a solemn conclave with Trudy and her mother.

"Mrs. Lawson," he began, "you knew I was Aunt Charlotte's heir? Broomfield is now mine and I intend to come and live there. If you have no objection, Nancy and I can be married quite soon. May we go ahead and make arrangements?"

With no hesitation Trudy's mother replied: "It will make me very happy, Roy. Trudy, too. It has always been her aim to have the family all together."

Trudy nodded eagerly. "Yes, indeed, Roy. It will be lovely to have you and Nancy close at hand . . . Lord and Lady of the Manor."

Roy smiled. "I don't intend to be idle, though. I'll have to give up my college post, of course, but now I'll be able to pursue another occupation, one after my own heart. I've been studying the trends in modern education and will probably write a book on the subject."

"Splendid!" exclaimed Trudy. "And you'll have all the time in the world to do it, not like me and my poetry, which I never write now at all."

"The day will come," he prophesied. "But that's not all I came to talk about. You people will be hearing from my aunt's lawyer. I have seen her will and she has made one or two bequests. There's five hundred pounds for you and Derek, Trudy, and another sum for the mission, to buy a new organ."

Trudy's eyes filled. "How kind! Last time I saw your aunt, she said Derek ought to have a car. Imagine her remembering that, when she was so ill."

"She must have remembered about David too," Roy went on. "There's mention of the old coachhouse, which she specially wants him to have for a pottery."

Trudy was quite overcome. "But the coachhouse is on your property, Roy. Are you sure it will be all right?"

"I'll be delighted. That old place has been empty for years. A use ought to be found for it, and a creative use is better than any."

"Your aunt's sentiments exactly," was the reply.

After Roy had gone, Trudy and her mother discussed his news.

"This is going to make a difference to us, isn't it, Mum? How do you feel about arranging a wedding for your younger daughter? I suppose Roy's people will expect something grand."

"I hope not too grand," was the reply.

Trudy was naturally excited about that five hundred pounds and the prospect of getting a car. She talked it over with Derek at night.

"We can get quite a good car for that, or even less if you'd like to keep something for emergencies," she suggested.

Characteristically, Derek replied: "We'll take time to think about it, Trudy. That money might be needed for something else. It would be a nice little nest egg."

Impatient Trudy give a tiny scowl. "That's you all over, Derek! Don't you see, if we hang on too long, we'll never get a car at all!"

But such talk made no impression on Derek, who never did anything in a hurry. With an arm round her he said placatingly:

"Trudy, love, we're talking about something we haven't got. We'll probably have to wait ages for the money. Lawyers are notoriously slow."

Trudy sighed. "So are bankers, apparently!" As for herself, the minute she pictured a thing, she wanted it to come true immediately.

It was not often that the pair did not see eye to eye. When the rare occasion occurred, Trudy had learned from experience that argument and even tears would not shift Derek from his standpoint. She had to use subtler methods if she wanted her own way, but in the main she came round to his point of view. As for the car, it could wait; as Derek said, they hadn't even got the money. But she had no intention of giving up the idea, no indeed!

A sparkling letter came from Nancy, full of plans for the wedding. She would like to have it in the village church where Roy's aunt had been a member. There would only be a few relatives of his present and it was to be a quiet wedding, please. Her mother was not to go to any expense.

This was a great relief to the family at Ardenlea. They

were leading a very busy life. Ping was back home and had started college again. He and Derek had to set off early in the morning, which meant a still earlier rise for Trudy. Feeling that her mother needed a rest, she insisted that she have breakfast in bed.

Sometimes the twins woke them very early indeed. Emerging from a deep sleep one Sunday morning, Trudy looked at her watch. It was only seven o'clock, but disturbing sounds were already coming from the next room, so she tumbled out of bed and went in to investigate. Mark was standing up in his cot chuckling, but poor Matthew was bathed in tears. It was only too plain that the milder twin had been struck by Mark's plastic duck which he had pitched into his cot.

"Naughty Mark!" Trudy proceeded to soothe the injured twin, laying him down with the injunction to go 'Sleepy bye-byes'. Obediently, Matthew closed his eyes, but when she tried the same tactics with Mark he merely laughed in her face and sat up again.

Oh well, she might as well dress and start the day. Going to the window she pulled aside the curtains and looked out. It was a typical autumn morning, hazy but fine, with a nip in the air. Though it was not yet fully light, the contents of the garden were clearly visible, from the clumps of bronze chrysanthemums to the pale helio of michaelmas daisies.

But there was something missing in the garden. Trudy looked again, rubbing her eyes. It definitely wasn't there, the precious seat that all the fuss had been about. The anniversary present from Derek had been placed with its back to the hedge on the day of their removal, and had stayed there ever since.

But it wasn't there now.

Late last night when everyone was asleep, it must have been removed. By whom? She did not have to seek for an answer. She went back and shook Derek's arm.

"Wake up, Derek! There's been a thief in the night!"

He sat up with a start. "What's that? A thief?"

"The seat has gone," she told him. "Our precious garden seat!"

"The seat? Oh, nonsense." Reluctantly he got out of bed and staggered to the window. "H'm, it seems to have disappeared right enough. It was there last night, wasn't it?"

"Yes, it was, and I know who stole it. I told you Mrs. Rice made threats—"

He laughed. "You don't think Mrs. Rice would lug away a heavy thing like that?"

"No, but she would hire someone else to do it. Derek, we've got to get it back!"

He rumpled his hair. "No good worrying about it at the moment. Let's get some more sleep."

"Well, perhaps you can sleep, but I can't! The first minute I'm able, I'm going up to demand that seat back."

Derek's face went stern. "Trudy, that would be coming down to the woman's own level. You can't do that."

"Well, what can I do, then?"

"Nothing in the meantime. Later, you might send a polite note."

Trudy argued that a polite note would have no effect. "A lawyer's letter is the only thing she would understand!"

"No," declared her husband. "I won't have my wife mixed up in a common row. It would be better to ignore the whole thing."

"But the seat is ours!" wailed Trudy.

"Undoubtedly! She is probably the kind of woman who loves a fight, Trudy. Give her the fight and you'll be playing her game. By doing nothing you might make her feel ashamed."

"Small chance of that!" It was all very well for Derek to talk, he hadn't had to listen to the lady's rude remarks. She wasn't going to give in so easily. She could do nothing today, as it was Sunday, but tomorrow she was determined to visit Mrs. Rice and demand her seat back.

Usually she enjoyed the walk to the hall with Derek, but today everything was wrong. It was beginning to rain, her shoes were hurting her and she felt tired and out of sorts.

Derek could hardly get a word out of her and soon he gave it up. Esther, who was waiting at the gate of the hall noticed the gloom.

"Who stole your scone, Trudy?" she asked with a laugh.

"It's not my scone that's been stolen," was the reply. "I'll tell you about it later, Esther."

Derek had asked Ping to take the morning service. Eva was playing the organ today and Trudy caught them smiling at each other before the service began. These two were very much in love and could not hide it.

From the moment Ping announced the first hymn Trudy felt an easing of the tension within her, for it was a hymn she had always loved.

'Breathe on me, Breath of God; Fill me with life anew, That I may love what Thou dost love, and do what Thou wouldst do.'

As the service went on her heart was stilled and she was able to think calmly. Ping chose the reading from the fifth Chapter of Matthew, beginning at the 38th verse:

"Ye have heard that it hath been said

An eye for an eye and a tooth for a tooth—"

How well she knew what was coming!

"But I say unto you, That ye resist not evil; But whosoever shall smite thee on thy right cheek, Turn to him the other also."

And later—

"Love your enemies, bless them that curse you,
Do good to them that hate you, and pray for them
which despitefully use you."

The reading ended—"Be ye therefore perfect, even as your Father which is in heaven is perfect."

So often had she heard the passage that she knew it by heart. She believed that in the chapter from which it was taken lay the very essence of Christianity. Yet here she was, believing in one thing yet practising another. For she was not turning the other cheek; she was not praying for the one who was despitefully using her. And if she went on feeling like this about Mrs. Rice, she was not a real Christian.

"I've failed," she thought. "Please God, forgive me, and I'll try again. Help me to be perfect, even as You are perfect."

At the end of the meeting, Esther took her by the arm.

"Whatever it was that was stolen from you, I can see you feel differently about it now."

"Yes," she agreed, "and I'll go on feeling differently."

To Derek on the way home she confided: "I'm sorry I was so disagreeable this morning. You were quite right. We'll forget about that seat."

He was surprised. "Are you sure, Trudy? We could at least report it to the police. Perhaps it wasn't Mrs. Rice after all."

She shook her head. "I'm sure it was, but I'd rather turn the other cheek. I've never really tried to win over Mrs. Rice. I may do it yet—"

"That's more like my Trudy talking," said Derek happily.

12

WHEN TRUDY HAD MADE UP HER MIND TO do a thing, however difficult, she executed it promptly. It was the only way to get it off her mind. So, the very next day, she left the twins with her mother and made her way uphill to her old home. What she was going to say to Mrs. Rice she had no idea, but peace must be made between them. If she did not make the first move, then nobody would.

Ringing the bell at the foot of the stair, she stood waiting. From this point she could see a bit of the back garden which used to be their own. Memories came flooding back; the return from their honeymoon, the plans she and Derek had for the garden, and how they had nearly quarrelled because Derek was so long getting started to dig. A lot of work had been put into it and they had just got things to their liking when the blow fell and now the Rices were enjoying the fruits of their labours. It was hardly fair.

Nobody seemed to be coming to the door. With great daring, Trudy left her stance to peep round the house and get a good look. The flowers they had planted seemed to smile at her like old friends and there in a sunny spot against the wall was the garden seat—*her* seat. Suddenly all her resolutions were swamped by a renewed feeling of anger. She stood there with her hands clenched battling hard to overcome it, but she could not do it, not by herself.

"I'll have to get help," she thought. "I'll have to pray. Please God, give me patience; tell me what I should say to this woman to make her a friend instead of an enemy."

Then she came back to the entrance just as the door opened at the top of the stairs. Mrs. Rice looked down and, seeing her, immediately stiffened.

"Well?" she demanded. "What do you want here?"

Still battling, Trudy asked: "May I come up, Mrs. Rice?"

"Stay where you are," was the reply, "or I'll set Jackie at you."

"Do that if you like," said Trudy, ascending the stair. "But I must speak to you."

For answer Mrs. Rice threw open the door and her dog sprang out. Trudy's first instinct was to turn and flee, but something made her stand firm. She held out a hand to the dog.

"Hello, Jackie! How are you, old boy?" And she patted the growling little creature with a steady hand. Fondling its silky ears she spoke to it in a soothing voice till it quietened down and actually licked her hand.

"Jackie likes me," she said simply.

The other looked completely taken aback.

"I wish you liked me, too," Trudy added.

Mrs. Rice sniffed. "You came about the garden seat, didn't you?"

"Not exactly," was the reply.

"Because if you expect me to hand it back, you'll be disappointed. Possession is nine points of the law."

Trudy smiled brightly. "I don't set much store by that kind of law. But you may keep the seat if you want it all that much, Mrs. Rice."

The other stared disbelievingly. "Just what is your little game?" she asked.

"It's not a game, I mean it. Mrs. Rice, you can't know many people here. Would you care to meet my mother?"

"I know all the people I want to know," she answered shortly.

Trudy tried again. "Well, if you ever feel you need someone to talk to, my mother is nearly always at home. You know the house—Ardenlea. It's by the burn at the foot of the hill."

"I know the house perfectly well," she was informed. "Thank you for the invitation but I shall not be taking advantage of it."

And with that, Mrs. Rice pulled Jackie into the house and closed the door.

"A lot of good that did," mused Trudy on the way home. "Still, it taught me something; that I can smother my feelings if I like, also that one need not be afraid of a yappy little dog. Jackie's bark is worse than his bite. Perhaps his mistress's is the same. Time will tell!"

When she got back she told her mother of the encounter.

"In the unlikely event of Mrs. Rice calling here, you'll be nice to her, Mum?"

But she knew perfectly well that the plea was unnecessary. Never in her life had Mrs. Lawson turned a stranger from her door.

All at once, it seemed, they were in the midst of preparations for the wedding.

Roy came north to install himself at Broomfield and naturally his mother came with him. Nancy followed later to stay at Ardenlea and get busy with her trousseau. Her arrival was a day for rejoicing. Trudy and she had a heart-to-heart talk in the little bedroom where her possessions were.

"Well, Nancy, it's coming sooner than you thought! Are you very happy?"

Her sister nodded. "In spite of everything, yes, I am."

"What do you mean—in spite of—?"

Nancy sat down on the bed. "Well, for one thing, it was sad about Aunt Charlotte, wasn't it? I was just getting to know her."

"Yes, we all miss her very much."

"The other thing is, of course, Roy's mother. She's going to live with us. I couldn't say no, Trudy. It's such a big house, there ought to be plenty of room. But I'm dreading it all the same."

Trudy quite understood. She had seen enough in the summer of these two conflicting natures to make her apprehensive. But in the meantime, nothing ought to cloud the present happiness of the couple.

Nancy agreed. "We love each other very much and that's the main thing."

"Perhaps your love for Roy will help you to understand his mother, Nancy, just as her love for him should help her to understand you."

"There's not much chance of that," was the sad reply.

"You might win her round. I'm having a tough job myself trying to make friends with the Mrs. Rice who took over our house," and Trudy described her latest attempt.

Nancy was amused. "Good for you, but I'm afraid the two cases are different. I must try to be more like you and keep my temper, though. Usually, I've got to blurt out what I think and no bones about it, but for Roy's sake I'm going to try to be patient. Last time we were here he and I nearly quarrelled, remember? When Aunt Charlotte died that was all forgotten. We are closer than ever now."

"I'm very pleased to hear it. When will you be seeing Roy?"

"At Broomfield this evening. Will you come with me? Talk to Mrs. Melrose and give me a chance to get Roy to myself?"

Trudy, willing to do anything to smooth her path, put the twins to bed early and left Derek and her mother in charge. The two girls made their way up the hill arm-in-arm. Winter was almost on them and there was frost in the air, but there were nearly always flowers blooming in the Broomfield garden. Roy had retained the services of the gardener and everything was neat and tidy.

"Elsa the housemaid is still here, too," remarked Nancy as they went up the drive. "Aunt Charlotte had a cook as well, but I intend to do the cooking myself."

"Will you be making many changes in the house?" Trudy asked her.

"Not in the meantime, except to bring the kitchen up to date. I'm sure the old house has feelings and would hate too many innovations."

"Exactly my sentiments."

At that moment they noticed a figure sliding out from the back of the house and making stealthily for a side gate.

Nancy caught her sister's arm. "Trudy, who can that be? He's here for no good!"

"Quite right. Let's go after him!" And they sprinted along to cut off the intruder.

"Hi! Stop there!" shouted Nancy.

The strange thing was that he did stop, which no guilty person would have done. Suddenly his laugh rang out.

"Well, if it's not my little sisters! You girls did give me a start!"

They gazed in astonishment at the shaggy, bearded face, the overalls all daubed with clay.

"David, you're a perfect disgrace!" scolded Trudy. "I'm ashamed to own you. What are you doing here?"

"Making a start in my pottery of course. Come and see it! Won't take a minute."

They followed him to the coachhouse, which had been repaired and adapted for his use. Inside was a large bare apartment with a strong aroma of wet clay and there on a wooden platform was a huge mound of the stuff ready for modelling. A potter's wheel stood beside it and along the shelves were some unfired specimens of vases or 'pots' as David called them.

"So this is where you play yourself," remarked Trudy.

David pretended to be hurt. "It's jolly hard work, I'm telling you! Feel the weight of that clay—" and he put a lump into her hands which she promptly let go.

"Ugh! This is my best coat, thank you!"

"I thought you would be more sympathetic," he grumbled. "You don't understand about potting at all. It's one of the oldest creative arts. The potter's wheel hasn't changed for thousands of years. Look, this is how it works," and he gave them a demonstration, pedalling away with his foot to turn the wheel and shaping the clay on top to achieve an artistic shape.

"Of course," he explained, "these pots have got to be fired. I'll have to have them done in Firton, but some day I'll have a kiln of my own and then I'll really be in business."

Trudy asked: "You don't mean you'd think of giving up your steady job, David?"

"Why not?" he asked defiantly. "I'm sick and tired of routine. I'd much prefer to work for myself, keep my own hours."

"Sure," observed Nancy, "sleeping in till noon and up all night, I suppose." She and Trudy were always inclined to take David's schemes with a pinch of salt.

"A typically sisterly remark," he grunted. "Esther wouldn't say that! She's all in favour."

"She would be," Trudy commented. Surely David would not be rash enough to throw up his bread-and-butter job for a risky venture like this? He must have been joking.

When at length Trudy and Nancy rang the bell of Broomfield, Roy answered it, taking Nancy in his arms and kissing her fondly. When his mother appeared, he let her go, however.

Mrs. Melrose held out her hand. "How are you, Nancy and Trudy? Welcome to Broomfield!"

She took them into the downstairs lounge which was small and intimate. Trudy had been in it often and guessed that it would be a favourite room with the pair, when they were man and wife. After a short time Roy got to his feet and pulled his fiancée to hers.

"We're going to look round the house, Nancy and I, to see what needs to be done. Come along, love!"

The two of them went out, leaving Trudy with his mother. Mrs. Melrose did not seem too pleased, but she only remarked:

"We might as well have a talk, Trudy! You know Nancy better than I do. I wonder if she realises just what she is taking on?"

Trudy answered readily, "Oh yes, Mrs. Melrose. Nancy is quite aware of her responsibilities, and I'm sure she will make Roy a good wife."

"She seems so young and inexperienced," sighed the other. "However, I shall be here to lend a helping hand. The younger generation can learn so much from the old."

Trudy replied; "Yes, indeed. And the old can learn from the young, too."

Roy's mother did not take this too well. "No doubt, in some things, but nothing can take the place of experience."

"Some kinds of wisdom," maintained Trudy, "don't need experience. They come instinctively with love."

With raised eyebrows, "Well, if you're going to argue about it—"

"Sorry," said Trudy. "I'm always getting into arguments."

"It seems to be a Lawson failing," declared Mrs. Melrose.

In the ensuing conversation it became evident to Trudy that although the house belonged to Roy, Mrs. Melrose regarded herself as its mistress. The way she had said 'Welcome to Broomfield' made that clear. Would she be prepared to give way when Nancy was Roy's wife?

Doubts were forgotten however, as the wedding day drew

near. Nothing could withstand Nancy's high spirits. Every minute was occupied in shopping, sewing, visiting the dressmaker and hairdresser, receiving presents and writing letters of thanks. As Roy had his aunt's car, transport was no problem and Trudy was pleased to see them go off together with no third person to interfere.

The others had a busy time, too, sending out invitations and receiving visitors. Eva was to be Nancy's bridesmaid and there were great deliberations about what she would wear, the choice falling on a long frock of eggshell blue with a band of forget-me-nots round her hair.

Nancy herself chose the traditional white, and when the great morning arrived Trudy was the one who helped her to dress. There on the bed was her mother's wedding veil which she herself had worn on her own momentous day.

"Do you remember the night before my wedding, Nancy? You begged for a last peep at my frock."

Her sister nodded her dark head. "I remarked that marriage was such a great adventure one ought to approach it in fear and trembling. But you were so calm, Trudy. You had no fear, you said, for 'perfect love casteth out fear'."

"Yes, and I found it true. As long as you love Roy and he loves you, you need have no fear either," and she kissed her sister.

At last the bride was ready and Tam the Taxi was at the door, his vehicle decorated with ribbons and orange blossom. Trudy helped her sister inside, then took her own seat, and Ping and her mother joined them. The twins, too young to know that a wedding was a solemn occasion, had been left in charge of Peggy Carson.

As they set off for the nearby church, the sun shone out, a good omen. A little group was waiting for them in the vestibule, including David, who was to give the bride away. In his immaculate lounge suit and neatly trimmed beard, he was a credit to the family, for once! Eva was there too, also Esther, anxiously supervising her offspring in their rôle of train bearers.

Inside the pretty little church Trudy sat beside her mother and Ping. When the organ began to play Roy, looking rather nervous, took his place beside the 'best man', a young lecturer friend from London. Now came the moment everyone was waiting for. To the strains of the Wedding March, a radiant Nancy walked up the aisle on David's arm with Eva and the children behind.

The village people in the back pews declared afterwards they had never seen a prettier wedding. But Trudy saw it all through a mist, for she was recalling her own wedding and the vows she had made that day. Derek must be remembering too, for he laid his hand on top of hers and held it firmly.

"To have and to hold from this day forward, for better or for worse, for richer, for poorer, in sickness and in health, to love and to cherish, till death us do part—"

The beautiful words found an answering response in their hearts. And there was Mum, her lips trembling, but holding back the tears just as she had done for Trudy. Ping, too, was looking extremely solemn, though his eyes were more for Eva than for the bride.

The hymn which followed 'Oh Perfect Love', was a moving climax to the ceremony.

'Grant them the joy that brightens earthly sorrow;
Grant them the peace which calms all earthly strife,
And to life's day the glorious unknown morrow
That dawns upon eternal love and life.'

13

NANCY'S WEDDING WAS A HIGHLIGHT IN THE history of the Lawson family. It had an effect on more people than the bride and bridegroom. Ping was one of them.

It was only the second wedding he had ever attended. The first was Trudy's and he had considered it a lot of fuss for nothing. Now that he was older and knew what it was to fall in love, the whole ceremony took on a deeper meaning that made him exceedingly thoughtful.

He knew now for a certainty that he had the same feeling for Eva as Derek had for Trudy and Roy for Nancy. As children he'd had a very tender spot for little Eva, who followed him round so devotedly, and when they met again in Hetherton, theirs had been a happy companionship. But it had taken the episode in Carencross to really open his eyes. There was no doubt about it, Eva was the girl he wanted to marry.

Was it fair to tie her down, however? Her mother had other ambitions for her and Eva herself might someday regret giving up her glittering prospects. Ping had decided to curb his longings in the meantime. He had told Eva that she came first with him, so at least they had an understanding.

But Nancy's wedding changed everything. During the ceremony Ping's eyes never left Eva's face. She was so beautiful that day, lovelier than he had ever seen her. He felt unworthy of her; he wasn't even good-looking, not like brother David or that 'best man' of Roy's who had come up from London, Ernest Owen, who had an ease of manner and a sophistication which must surely appeal to a girl like Eva. Ping noticed it particularly at the wedding luncheon in Firton, for Ernest Owen was sitting next to Eva, claiming all her attention; and Eva was chatting and smiling to him as if he were the only man in the world.

This was rank jealousy, thought Ping; hadn't she every right to be nice to Roy's best man, especially as she was the bridesmaid? It wasn't any worse than when he had neglected her to attend to Doris Lambert. He was beginning to understand what Eva must have gone through at that time and his heart grew tender. She had suffered because she was not sure of him, and now he was suffering because he was not sure of her.

"But of course I'm sure of her," he thought. "Didn't she practically confess that she loved me? I read it in her eyes, that day in London." But perhaps this handsome stranger from the world outside was already stealing her heart away from him? Ping became very gloomy indeed. "I've got to feel sure! I shan't know a minute's peace till I do!"

And so it happened that after the festivities were over and the happy pair went off on the first stage of their honeymoon to Majorca, Ping looked round for Eva. She was with Ernest Owen in the lounge of the hotel.

"Coming home now, Eva?" asked Ping. Eva stammered and blushed while her companion put in—

"The fact is, a few of us have arranged to go to an orchestral concert in the town hall. Will you join us?"

There was no reason why Ping should refuse, for he was genuinely fond of music, but he suddenly took what their old housekeeper Becky called 'the sturdies'.

"Sorry, I haven't got the time," he replied.

He returned home with Trudy and Derek, who were anxious about the twins. The minute they got in, Ping made an excuse to go up to his study. He opened his books and started to read, but the words were a meaningless jumble so he gave it up.

Much later, when Trudy and Derek were preparing to retire for the night, they were startled by the sound of Ping rushing downstairs and through the hall as if wild horses were chasing him. Then the front door opened and shut with a bang and flying footsteps were heard outside, gradually dying away.

"What's eating him?" enquired Derek.

Trudy had not been blind. "Something to do with Eva, probably."

"People in love are a bit daft," he observed.

"Weren't you a bit daft yourself?" she asked softly.

He sat down very close and put his arm round her. "I'm still daft about you, Trudy!"

"And I about you. More so, after listening to the wedding service today. It was like a 'refresher course'. Don't you think there should be a refresher course in marriage vows for everybody, when things get stale?"

"Yes, but things will never get stale where you are," laughed her husband.

Meanwhile, Ping was haring it up the hill to the Coopers' house. Surely Eva would be home? If he didn't speak to her tonight he wouldn't sleep a wink.

He had just reached the gate when he heard a car coming up behind him. Stepping into the shadow of some trees he saw, as he had expected, the car stop at the gate. Ernest Owen got out and then helped Eva to alight. He seemed to hold her hand for a very long time, but what he was saying Ping could not hear.

Then he sped away in the car and Eva was alone. In an instant Ping was beside her, grasping her arm.

"Eva, I've got to talk to you!"

She gave a start. "Ping what a fright you gave me!"

He humbly apologised. "What a lout I am!"

She laughed—like silver bells. "Don't call yourself that; it's not true."

"It is. I'm everything that's stupid. It's a wonder you like me even a little."

"But I don't like you a little," she declared. "I like you a lot."

Ping took her hands in his and said solemnly: "Do you mean that? Do you like me better than the man you've just been holding hands with?"

"I haven't!" she protested. "But of course I like you better. Ernest Owen is just a flatterer; he says things he doesn't mean. But you, Ping—you are genuine. Like in the Bible—your 'yea is yea' and your 'nay is nay'."

Ping did not know how it happened but suddenly she was in his arms. How small she was, how soft and sweet! Overcome with the emotion he had tried so hard to check, he murmured, his cheek against her hair—

"Eva, my own precious girl, do you love me enough to marry me?"

The face she turned to his was pale in the lamplight, but the look in her eyes was something he would never forget.

"I've been longing to hear you say that, Ping!"

"You're sure, Eva? Life won't be easy married to a gomeril like me!"

"I don't want life to be easy," she whispered. "An easy life is an empty one. I'd rather it were full and difficult."

He took her face between his hands and gazed deep into those shining eyes. "The first time I saw you, Eva, on our island holiday, I said to Trudy—'That little girl looks like an angel'."

She laughed shakily. "I was anything but an angel!"

"I think I must have loved you even in those far-off days. Do you remember the fun we used to have on the Silver Beach? We'll go back there for our honeymoon, shall we?"

Eva replied in a happy whisper, "Oh, Ping! But that's a long time ahead."

"I'm afraid so," he said sadly. "A very long time. Can you wait, Eva? I wasn't going to bind you to anything, but if it's your wish, we can get engaged."

"Yes, Ping I'd love that. But let's keep it to ourselves for a little. It's such a lovely secret!"

They clung together, unwilling to break up the magic moment. It would never be quite like this again.

Nancy and Roy were away for three weeks. On the day of their return they came down to Ardenlea for 'High Tea'. It was a real family gathering, for Esther and David were there with their little girls and Eva had been invited, too.

Trudy had prepared a very large steak pie and was inspecting its progress in the kitchen when Nancy came in to say:

"Can I do anything to help?"

"No, thank you! Save your energies for the future," she was told. "You look well, Nancy; I needn't ask if you are happy."

"I never dreamt of such happiness," sighed her sister. "Roy and I were made for each other. If only the future could be like those last three weeks!"

Trudy closed the oven door, her face pink with the heat. "Married life is no honeymoon! But you can keep the honeymoon spirit."

"I hope so. Trudy, it's begun already. Roy's mother has got me all ruffled, in spite of my good resolutions. I wanted to cook lunch today, but she says it's too soon, she must show me what to do first; Roy likes this and Roy doesn't like that and so on. I've got to find out for myself, Trudy, what Roy likes. I won't be told by his mother!"

Trudy sat down thoughtfully on the kitchen stool. "Poor Nancy. I simply don't know what I'd do in your place. Complain to Roy, probably."

"No, I shan't drag Roy in, if I can help it. I'll battle on

alone and try to curb my tongue."

"That's right," said Trudy. "There's some good advice in Proverbs. Let me think. 'Whoso keepeth his mouth and his tongue keepeth his soul from troubles'."

"I'll remember that, Trudy. Thanks ever so! Do you mind if I use you for letting off steam?"

"I'm here to be used," was the reply.

The table in the big room was extended to its uttermost for the meal, and the twins were set up in their high chairs. There were plenty of alarms and excursions, but on the whole the children behaved well and there was a feeling of jollity which was always in the air when the family got together. Afterwards, the men helped with the washing-up and the kitchen was very crowded indeed, but miraculously there were no dishes broken.

Soon the twins started to get cross. "I'll take them up to bed now," said Trudy.

Her mother halted her. "Could you wait a few minutes? I thought since we were altogether, we might have one of our old-fashioned hymn singings."

"Good idea," declared Ping. "Action, please!"

Nancy took her old place at the piano and Trudy looked out the hymnbooks. When ready, Mrs. Lawson sat on a big chair and Trudy and Derek shared another. Esther and David occupied the couch with their daughters between them; Roy stood at the window and Ping and Eva beside the piano. The twins were parked on the floor, though they were not expected to stay put for long.

In former times it had always been Ping, the youngest, who chose the hymns.

"But I'm one of the old ones now," he said, smiling at Eva. "Some one else must choose, tonight."

Trudy Anne ran to him excitedly. "Me, Uncle Ping!"

"Very well, sweetie-pie. What is it to be?"

The small girl answered without hesitation: " 'If I come to Jesus.' I know that one."

"Then you shall sing it for us," said Uncle Ping.

Nancy played softly while the child sang in a clear, sweet treble the simple words of the hymn—"If I come to Jesus, he will make me glad—" Then they all joined in the chorus:

"If I come to Jesus, happy shall I be;
He is gently calling little ones like me."

Esther's eyes shone with a lovely light as she listened to her first-born make her 'debut' as a soloist in the family circle. Her glance met that of Mrs. Lawson and they exchanged smiles. The latter was very much moved, for it was a great occasion to have them all round her like this. Her eyes went from one to another: from David her eldest, who lived in a world of his own, the world of the artist; then to Trudy the dreamer, who had had to give up some of her dreams to take on the tasks of mother-hood. For Nancy at the piano, dreams had just come true, but inevitably there would be some kind of awakening; one could not live in the clouds for ever!

Mrs. Lawson had a shrewd idea of conditions at Broom-field and she felt anxious about her impulsive younger daughter, so easily could one false step disturb the serenity of these first months of marriage. Difficult enough when a couple were on their own, they were much more com-plicated when a third person intervened. She could only hope and pray that some solution would be found.

She prayed for them all, every day; for her youngest, too, the little boy who was little no longer but still her Ping, as single-minded as ever in his determination to tell the world about the wonderful Jesus, whose teaching was the only hope for mankind.

They finished up by singing a hymn which was one of Ping's favourites: 'God is working His purpose out, as year succeeds to year': the last verse was like a clarion call:

"*All we can do is nothing worth, unless God blesses the deed;*

Vainly we hope for the harvest-tide, till God gives life to the seed;

Yet nearer and nearer draws the time: the time that shall surely be,

When the earth shall be filled with the glory of God, as the waters cover the sea."

For two minutes everyone was quiet, then Trudy got to her feet.

"I'll simply have to get these twins to bed!"

She was stopped again, this time by Ping. With Eva's hand in his he walked to the centre of the room. It had been arranged between them that this was the big moment.

"We have an announcement to make," he said solemnly.

All eyes were turned in their direction. Nancy laughed:

"You needn't make it. It's obvious!"

"Nevertheless we insist. Don't we, Eva?"

Blushing, she smiled up at him. "Yes, Ping, go on!"

"We're engaged," he said. "We're going to be married —some day."

Everybody jumped up and began to congratulate them. There was a great deal of kissing and much laughter. Trudy Anne ran up to Ping and hugged his knees, then to everyone's amusement, she asked:

"Can I be your train-bearer, Uncle Ping?"

It was as much as Trudy and Derek could do to tear themselves away, each carrying a twin.

"So now," remarked Derek, after they were tucked in, "you needn't worry about Ping and Eva any more."

"I suppose not," was the reply. "Still, there's just one snag that no one seems to have thought of. What is Eva's mother going to say about all this?"

14

Winter wore on, bringing frost and snow, so that the twins had to be clad from head to toe in layers of woollies that made them look like little fat balloons, especially Mark, whose nickname 'Bubble' had begun to stick.

From time to time they held more family get-togethers, sometimes at Ardenlea, less often at Broomfield. The truth was, they never felt quite free in Nancy's home, for Mrs. Melrose was always present and she did not seem to understand children. It was impossible to keep the four little ones under restraint all the time. They spilled their food, ran about noisily, and sometimes they broke things. This did not worry Nancy so much as it did her mother-in-law. Anything that was broken had always been specially dear to Aunt Charlotte, so Mrs. Melrose declared. It made Trudy very nervous about visiting the house and Nancy, who loved little children, felt aggrieved. She was having a hard battle to keep things going smoothly and it was beginning to tell on her.

For the newly engaged couple, there were set-backs too. Eva postponed writing to her mother, fearing her reactions, till finally Trudy persuaded her it was only her duty. So Eva and Ping each wrote a letter. "I have always loved Ping and always will," wrote Eva, "so I hope you will give us your blessing." Ping for his part, made a manly request for permission to marry Eva, when he was in a position to do so.

One afternoon Eva came running down the hill from the Bank with the reply to their letters in her hand.

Trudy, opening the door, saw by her trembling lip that the news was not favourable.

"How can a mother be so cruel!" Eva exclaimed. "Read this, Trudy."

"My dear Eva," she read, "what is this nonsense? Bad enough for you to reject your mother's offer of a comfortable home and everything that money can buy, but to ruin your future by getting tied up with a penniless student is sheer folly. I certainly shall not agree to this engagement, and hope you will see reason and break it off at once. These Hetherton people have had a bad influence on you from the start. Hoping to hear that you have come to your senses, Your loving mother."

"She isn't my loving mother at all," protested Eva. "She never took the slightest interest in me till a few years ago, when she realised that I might be a credit to her. I could, too, had she been more sympathetic and less worldly. I was ready to love her, but it wasn't love she wanted; so why should I take any notice of what she says? This is not going to make the slightest difference, Trudy. I'll write and tell her so."

Trudy was on her side, of course, but it was not the best augury for either Eva or Ping to go against the wishes of her mother. They were happy enough now not to care, but what of the future? Trudy discussed the problem with Derek that night after the others were in bed, but they could see no solution to it.

"And talking about the future," she added at last, "what about our own, Derek?"

Derek, recovering from a bad cold, was not in the best of fettle. He closed his book with a sigh. When Trudy was in a talking mood, then goodbye to reading.

"What do you mean, our future?" he asked obtusely.

"You know fine what I mean. We've got that money from Mrs. Scott Brown's estate. What are we going to do with it?"

He knew the question had been coming, but his answer was unhelpful.

"I thought we'd agreed to keep it for a nest egg."

"Derek Crawford, it was you who said that, not me! No, we're going to buy that car. No more bad colds waiting for buses. You and Ping can both get the use of it, and think how lovely it will be to take Mum and the twins for a run."

"Yes, I suppose so. Oh well, I'll see about it soon."

Trudy put an arm round his neck. "I know what your 'soon' is, Derek. Tam the Taxi was telling me about a good bargain in second hand cars, one with automatic gears, he says. Shall I ask him to bring it round on Saturday?"

Derek laughed. "You hustler, you! So you've got it all arranged? Tam may bring round the car, then, but I'm not promising anything."

Trudy hugged him tightly. "Just think, it will be in time for spring and summer. We can take the older mission folk for runs, too. Some of them haven't been out for long enough!"

Everything the Crawfords did had to be geared to the 'mission folk' and the work they loved. Thanks to the legacy, the old organ, which had emitted its last groan, was done away with and a new one installed. It was of the transistor type, with a fine range of tone and expression and very easy to play. It almost played itself, Esther declared, and she as organist ought to know.

Since her marriage Nancy had become an enthusiastic helper, too, her chief delight being her Sunday School class. She was never happier than when surrounded by children, the more the merrier. What more natural than that she should invite her class to tea?

But it was not so simple. When she presented herself at Ardenlea one forenoon, Trudy knew by her face that something was amiss.

"I simply don't know what to do, Trudy! I invited those kids, eight of them, for tea and games next Saturday. I didn't think it necessary to consult Roy's mother. Well, I don't have to consult her about everything, do I?" she asked stormily.

Trudy agreed that in this case it seemed hardly necessary. "Why, what happened?"

"Just this. When I informed her they were coming, she objected strongly. She said the kids would break up the place and Aunt Charlotte would never have stood for it."

Trudy smiled reminiscently. "I seem to remember Aunt Charlotte running a party for mothers once. They played hide-and-seek all over the house and she enjoyed it thoroughly."

"Really? I must tell Roy's mother, not that it would make any impression. Well, I said I was going on with the party, for the children would be disappointed otherwise. Had Roy given his permission? she asked. I said no, but he was sure to agree. Then do you know what she did?"

"I can guess," murmured Trudy.

"Yes, she went straight to Roy and told him what I had arranged without her knowledge. She did not approve and neither would Aunt Charlotte. Besides, she hadn't been well and the upset of a children's party would not be good for her."

"What's the matter with her, Nancy?"

"Nerves or something; I'm sure it's not serious. However, Roy asked me to put the thing off and for the sake of peace I agreed. I haven't told the kids yet, Trudy. They'll be terribly disappointed!"

Trudy considered. "They needn't be, Nancy. I'll tell you what, we'll have the party here. Mum won't mind."

Her face brightened. "Oh, Trudy, how good of you! You always come to the rescue. Now I'll be independent of Mamma Melrose. I've done my best to like her, Trudy, but I just don't seem to manage it. By the way, how are you getting on with your 'bête-noire', the lady at the Bank?"

"I hardly ever see her," was the reply, "and when I do, she carefully turns away. I asked her to visit us, but she has never shown up: Still, the thought of her doesn't make me burn the way it used to do."

"And the thought of your beloved flat?"

"I've got over that grudge," said Trudy slowly. "It wasn't her fault, after all, that her husband stepped into Derek's shoes. I'll always have a qualm about our first home, of course, but we'll get another of our own some day. In the meantime, Nancy, what do you think? We're going to buy a car!"

Nancy was delighted. "When, Trudy?"

"Tam the Taxi is bringing one round on Saturday. What time are you planning to have the party?"

Four o'clock, Nancy told her. She would collect the girls and bring them down. They discussed what they would give them to eat and what games they would play: and what about asking Esther and her two to share the fun?

Mrs. Lawson agreed heartily to their arrangements and when the day came, Trudy had a busy forenoon baking and preparing, while the twins, scorning sleep, did their best to hinder her efforts. Esther arrived at three with her contributions.

"Any chance of David coming along?" Trudy asked.

"Oh, he's all wrapped up in his clay," laughed her friend. "He's expecting his new kiln to arrive this afternoon and can think of nothing else."

"But he told me he had no money to buy a kiln."

"He was so keen to get one," explained Esther, "that I asked my father for a loan. Don't frown, Trudy! Dad was only too pleased."

Up till now, David had been too independent to borrow

money, but now it was different.

"This potting has gone to his head," declared Trudy. "He's threatened to throw up his steady job, Esther. You wouldn't let him, would you?"

"He is so gifted," sighed Esther, "I feel he ought to have his head."

"But it would take him years to make any kind of living at pottery!"

"You may be right," agreed Esther thoughtfully. "When I think of the money we go through in a week! You're more practical than I am, Trudy, yet you never used to be."

"I never had to be, till the babies came along; it's not natural to me at all," laughed Trudy. "All I know is that if your expenditure exceeds your income, the result is—misery, as Mr. Micawber put it."

At this juncture little Margaret, who was at the window, called out in her piping voice:

"A car at the gate, Mummy!"

And so it was, a very fine light grey car with Tam the Taxi at the wheel. Trudy called for Derek to come and look, and preceded him to the gate, lost in admiration.

"It's a lovely car, Tam!"

"Yes, Mrs. Crawford, a very fine model and as good as new."

Already Trudy saw herself and Derek, the proud owners, driving off light-heartedly to places they had longed to visit. What holidays they would have with the twins!

"Jump in, you and the mister," bade Tam. "You can't buy a car till you've driven in her first!"

"Yes, Trudy," urged Esther. "I'll hold the fort till you come back."

Derek sat beside Tam to study all the gadgets for driving and Trudy sat in the back. They were up the hill and out on the moor before she realised it. They travelled for miles, yet seemed to be home again in no time. She felt exhilarated beyond words, but Derek was his usual calm self.

"Yes," he observed when they stopped at the gate, "the engine runs very smoothly. The car's got a nice appearance, too. I'll think about it."

But Trudy did not want to think. "Couldn't we just say we'll have it, Derek?"

"No need to rush. Tam won't sell it to anyone else in the meantime, will you, Tam?"

Tam promised to reserve the car till Derek had made up his mind. As he drove off, Trudy turned to her husband disappointedly:

"Why did you let it go, Derek? Anything might happen!"

"I've got to have time," he told her.

"You've had time already, weeks and months!" They might have quarrelled then and there, but he pressed her arm fondly.

"I know that. Don't worry, Trudy, you'll get your car."

With that she had to be content. Anyhow, there was no chance to linger on it, for Nancy was there with her bunch of girls and things were already hectic.

They sat the children at the big table and the adults stood round to serve them and see that everybody got fair shares. Though most of the girls were shy to begin with, they soon expanded in the genial atmosphere and the food rapidly disappeared. Nancy was in her element, her vexations forgotten, and Trudy felt it was a shame that she could not be like this in her own home.

Nancy seemed to know the right kind of games to amuse the company. They had guessing games and such items as 'Musical Arms', in which the grown-ups took part, including Ping who had joined them. Nancy played the piano and the fun waxed fast and furious. Ping became like a little boy again, jumping about and stamping his feet till they had to restrain him. The twins, who had been put to bed,

116

simply refused to sleep and a quieter game had to be introduced. When the party was over and the visitors gone away, the four who were left sank gratefully on to chairs.

Sighed Trudy: "I'm absolutely exhausted! What about you, Mum?"

Mrs. Lawson rose. "I think I'll go to bed," she said wearily, and wishing them goodnight she left the room. Ping said he would do likewise and got up with a big yawn. As he was passing the window he stopped suddenly and bent down to examine the floor boards under the carpet.

"Anything wrong?" asked Trudy, not dreaming for a moment what the action portended.

Ping looked up, his face serious. "Derek, look at this. Some energetic person has jumped right through the floor!"

Sure enough, there was a hole there with signs of more caving in.

"That's you and your nonsense, Ping," scolded his sister. "What is Mum going to say?"

Derek was on his knees, testing the floor. Little bits of it were coming away in his hand.

"That's queer," muttered Trudy. "The wood's very soft, surely?"

"Yes," said Derek in bleak tones. "What we've got here is dry rot. If it's at all extensive, we're in for a big bill for repairs."

"A bill? How much?" his wife faltered.

"It might be hundreds of pounds," he declared.

His words were a bitter blow. Trudy and he exchanged meaningful glances. Each knew what the other was thinking.

"I—I suppose this means no car for us after all?" she said shakily.

"It looks like it," was the gloomy reply.

15

Trudy kept hoping against hope that Derek had made a mistake about the dry rot at Ardenlea, or at least that the floor could be repaired at small expense. Her hopes were doomed, however. When the builder whom Derek contacted came to inspect the damage, he told them that it had already spread quite seriously. If it were not eradicated immediately, the whole house would be affected.

To save Mrs. Lawson worry they made light of the matter, especially as her health was still poor.

"Cheer up, mother Lawson!" Derek urged her. "We'll have to put up with workmen about the house for a while, but it will soon be over!"

"Will it cost a lot?" Mrs. Lawson asked anxiously.

"I hope not, but in any case, that's our affair, not yours. It was in the arrangement that Trudy and I were responsible for all repairs."

She gave him a grateful smile. "You are a very satisfactory son-in-law, Derek. I couldn't wish for a better."

He put his arm round her shoulder. "And you are a lovely mother-in-law, Mrs. L! I'm a fortunate fellow."

At which Trudy observed with a laugh. "Forming a mutual admiration society, you two?"

She was trying hard to hide her disappointment at not getting that car. Her hopes had been so buoyed up! It had been within their grasp, only to be snatched away. She kept telling herself it was only a postponement, that they'd be sure to get a car some day but she had so wanted one, here and now! Still, she had to admit it was a good thing they had put off buying one; otherwise they'd have had nothing put by for this emergency. As for this dejected feeling, she would soon get over it. Forget about it, look on the bright side, she told herself.

She had much need to look on the bright side in the days which followed. It was bad enough having the floor up in the main room with workmen coming and going and draughts all over the place; and the kitchen never tidy because she was always making cups of tea—what an amount of tea those workmen consumed! But things got worse when, instead of the arrival of spring, the winter became even more severe. There was snow and slush and icy winds to contend with; Derek contracted another cold and the twins went down with it, too. Matthew consented to lie cosily in his cot, but restless Mark was up and down all the time giving voice to his discomfort.

Nancy came to the rescue more than once. She knew just how to amuse the ailing twins, and Trudy was grateful. But it was all too plain that Nancy was not happy. True to her word she 'used' Trudy as a safety valve and the stories of friction at Broomfield mounted up and up. In the main Nancy had managed to control her impulsive nature and give the soft answer, but the strain was beginning to tell.

There were visits from Esther, too. She was looking rather pale these days and always seemed to be tired.

"I'm trying to do without help in the house," she told Trudy. "I'm saving the money to have something to fall back on when David starts his pottery full time."

Trudy was doubtful about the wisdom of this. "But Esther, you know you've never been strong. You ought to reserve your strength, otherwise you'll flop and where will your family be then? It's a wonder David doesn't see that." But David saw nothing but his potter's wheel and his own rosy visions of the future.

"I don't know what's happened to everybody," Trudy

remarked to her husband that night as they sat in extreme discomfort in the living-room, beside a fire that refused to 'draw'. It had always been a poor chimney, not like the one in the big room, but of course they couldn't use the big room in its present state.

Derek gave a sepulchral cough. "What do you mean—happened?" he enquired.

"Well, it seems that a cloud with no silver lining has descended on the Lawsons."

"Not all of them," he grunted. "Ping's all right, isn't he?"

"Physically, yes. But he's terribly grumpy these days, don't you notice it?"

"Anybody would be grumpy in this weather with the wind howling outside and in. He'll get over it."

"It's to do with Eva," declared his wife. "You know she wrote to her mother saying she would never give up Ping. Well, it seems her mother's reply has upset them both. She is determined to force them apart, Derek."

Derek stretched out his hands to the feeble flames. "She can't do that if they are determined to stick together. This isn't the middle ages!"

Trudy smiled. "Oh, I don't suppose they'll be influenced by her. They know their own minds too well. But if they could get her approval it would make life easier for them both."

She stopped as a cry was heard from above. The twins were sleeping badly these nights. Wearily she made her way upstairs, took Mark from his cot lest he should wake his brother, and wrapping him in a shawl, walked about with him till he was quiet. Then she laid him down again and went back to make a hot drink for Derek. It seemed to ease his cough and he betook himself to bed saying he would be better in the morning.

Trudy stayed a little longer. It was so nice just to sit and do nothing for once in a way. She recalled the sunny fortnight in summer when there didn't seem to be a cloud in her sky.

"Oh well, it can't always be summer," she told herself. "Perhaps these clouds will soon pass away."

But there were darker days to come before that happened.

Going up to her bed, she paused for a moment in the hall beside her mother's door. She was sure she had heard a sound and stood very still listening. There it was again, a very slight sound like a moan. An icy hand seemed to clutch at her heart as she softly opened the door. Her mother sat up and switched on the bed light.

"Is that you, Trudy?" Her voice had a forced brightness.

"Yes, Mum." She went swiftly to her side. "Is there something the matter, dear?"

"Nothing at all," was the reply. "Why do you ask?"

"Because I heard you. You're in pain and you're keeping quiet about it. It's not fair; you've got to tell me what's wrong. Please!"

Her mother lay back, faintly smiling. "I daresay it's nothing much. I haven't been feeling too well lately, it's true. But you've got enough to cope with, Trudy, without another invalid on your hands."

"That's no excuse. Why shouldn't you be on my hands?" demanded Trudy. "I've been on yours often enough. Now, listen, you've got to let me telephone Dr. Murray, this very minute."

Mrs. Lawson caught her arm. "It's far too late, Trudy. Tomorrow perhaps. I'll be perfectly all right till then. I feel better already."

Trudy hesitated. "Are you quite sure? Then tell me what I can do to help you to sleep."

"Just read me the twenty-third Psalm."

Trudy opened the Bible which was always beside the bed, and read:

"The Lord is my Shepherd; I shall not want.
He maketh me to lie down in green pastures:
He leadeth me beside the still waters . . .
Yea, though I walk through the valley of the shadow
    of death
I will fear no evil: for thou art with me;
Thy rod and thy staff they comfort me . . ."

At the end, her mother lay quietly, her eyes closing.

"I will fear no evil, for thou art with me," she murmured. "Thank you, Trudy. Go to bed, now, there's a good girl."

Trudy crept upstairs, a lump in her throat. She blamed herself for letting her mother go on so long without medical attention, but Mum had been so sure her trouble would soon clear up and there had been so many other things to attend to.

In the morning, despite Mrs. Lawson's plea that she was better, Trudy phoned the doctor and he came almost immediately. A kindly man, he stayed chatting with the invalid, even letting out a cheerful laugh now and again so that Trudy, waiting in the hall, told herself it could not be serious. But when the doctor came out and spoke to her, she knew better.

"I'll have to get another opinion," he informed her. "The likelihood is that your mother will require an operation. Meanwhile, keep her in bed and keep her cheery, that's all you can do."

As she closed the door behind him, Trudy felt like going all to pieces. But a lot of good that would do! It wasn't the first time she had been faced with a sudden challenge. In the past, she had always managed to cope, and so it would be again. But not alone. She put up a little prayer:

"Help me, God, for I'm not strong enough in myself."

After that she felt much calmer and was able to go to

her mother and even start to tease her a little. Long faces would only distress her, she knew.

That was one of the hardest days Trudy had ever gone through. Derek had left early and so had Ping, neither of them knowing there was anything wrong. The workmen in the house seemed noisier than ever, the rain poured down relentlessly and there was no comfort anywhere. The twins, too, kept up a constant 'yammering', and indeed the only cheerful person was her mother, whose only anxiety was that she should not be a burden.

"As if a mother could be a burden! Certainly not a mother like you," Trudy informed her when she brought in her lunch tray.

"Soup? That's nice," said Mrs. Lawson. "It looks like 'hough' soup, made from Becky's recipe. She used to make it when any of us was ill, remember? How clever of you to think of it!" and to her daughter's delight she supped every drop of it.

After the meal Trudy asked the workmen to 'call it a day', as Dr. Murray was expected to return with a Consultant and the quieter it was the better. Fortunately, the twins consented to take a nap and everything was in order when the two doctors arrived.

While she waited anxiously for their verdict, Trudy wished she had rung up either Esther or Nancy to tell them what was afoot, for company would have made the time pass more quickly; but it was too late now. The time dragged by, every minute seeming an hour.

At last the waiting was over and the verdict pronounced. Tomorrow her mother would be taken to hospital in Firton. The ambulance would come for her about noon and she would probably be gone for three weeks or a month.

"Now then, you're not to worry," said Dr. Murray with a hand on her shoulder. "After this operation your mother should be better than ever. It's just a matter of patience."

When they departed, Trudy blinked away a few tears,

took the invalid a cup of tea, then went to the telephone to tell Nancy. Her sister joined her in no time and her practical common sense brought great comfort.

"Nancy, you're a nurse. Didn't you see this coming?" Trudy asked.

"I suspected it once or twice, but Mum is so good at covering up. Now, let's see, Trudy. You'll have to pack a suitcase for her. I'll tell you what to put in it."

Nancy came back next day to accompany the invalid in the ambulance and see her safely installed. Their mother declared she didn't know what all the fuss was about. Thousands of people had operations and hospitals were such pleasant places nowadays, it would be more like a holiday than anything else. And if those ambulance men thought they were going to carry her out on a stretcher, they had another think coming! She was quite able to walk, thank you. All in all, it was a perfectly cheerful leave-taking. Trudy and the twins waved farewell from the window.

"Gran-gran away ta-ta," lisped Mark solemnly. "Gran-gran come back soon?"

"Yes, Mark, quite soon," Trudy assured him chokily, as she wiped his nose and patted down his hair. The house seemed very empty already. The sooner these work-men were back the better!

Mrs. Lawson had her operation a day or two later and was reported to be 'fairly comfortable'. It wasn't much to go on, but Nancy assured them it was all that any-body could say meantime.

"She may be weak for a while, Trudy, but I'm sure there's nothing to worry about. They'd soon let you know if there was!"

All the same, Trudy was not prepared to see her mother quite so pale and listless when she went in to visit her next day. The smile was still there but she could not talk much and her daughter came away with a heavy heart. She was waiting for a bus to take her home when she recognised Roy Melrose's car stopping beside her.

He opened the door. "Going home, Trudy? Jump in."

"Thanks, Roy," and she seated herself. "You haven't got Nancy with you?"

"Not today. I've been at the reference library. How is your mother, Trudy?"

"They say she is 'comfortable'," was the reply, "but she looks very far away to me. Kind of hovering, as if she didn't know whether to come back to the world or not."

"You'll notice a difference next time you visit," he assured her as they drove out of the busy streets to the Hetherton road. "I'm so sorry about all this, Trudy. I'm fond of your mother, everybody is. She is such a good person, yet she doesn't thrust her goodness at you. You just feel it; it shines about her like an aura."

"That's exactly right. How well you put it, Roy!"

He drove on for a few minutes in silence, then turned to her:

"Now that I can talk to you alone, Trudy, I'd like to ask you something. It's about Nancy; she doesn't seem herself these days. Oh, I know she's upset about her mother, but it started long before that. She used to be so talkative and bright, the most outgoing person imaginable. Now she is withdrawn; it's as if something had come between us. I wonder if you, as her sister, have any clue?"

Trudy hardly knew what to say. If Roy, living so close to Nancy and his mother did not see what was happening, who was she to tell him? Yet for Nancy's sake perhaps she should drop a hint.

"If you really want to know, Roy, I'll tell you what I think. You'll forgive me for being frank?"

"It's what I want you to be, as frank as you like."

Trudy plunged in. "You say Nancy isn't open and free

the way she used to be, and it's true. She has been restricted beyond reason, not by you, Roy, but by your mother."

There, it was out. Roy gripped the wheel with tense hands.

"You think that? But I don't understand. Mamma is fond of Nancy. She is anxious to help her."

"In the way she wants, yes, but that kind of help isn't always helpful, if you see what I mean. Nancy wants to be free to make mistakes, especially in her own kitchen."

"But," he argued, "she is inexperienced and needs instruction."

She could almost hear his mother speaking; Roy had been well primed.

"Nancy knows a lot more than she gets credit for!" Trudy declared. "Hasn't she nursed sick people for years and cooked for them too? Surely she can be trusted to look after one man! You simply don't understand, Roy."

"Yes, what don't I understand?" he asked patiently.

"That a kitchen is a wife's kingdom and that she should be allowed to rule over it herself."

She did not look at him. Would he take offence and never speak to her again?

After a moment he replied thoughtfully: "There may be something in what you say. But what can I do about it?"

"Surely I don't have to tell you, Roy. You are Nancy's husband and her happiness lies in your hands."

In spite of the tension, Roy smiled. "Straight speaking from the Lawson front!"

They relapsed into silence and nothing more was said till they reached Ardenlea. Roy's face was thoughtful as he said goodbye.

"You've given me something to think about, Trudy."

"You're not angry with me, then?"

"I asked for it," was the quiet response.

16

THOUGH SAFELY OVER THE WORST, MRS. Lawson was slow to rally and for a time her family were anxious about her. Trudy took heart, however, when she visited the hospital one day to find her mother sitting up in a new pink bed jacket, busy with her knitting needles.

"Look, Trudy, it's a cardigan for one of the twins. I hope to finish two of them before I leave here. Isn't it a pretty shade of blue?"

Trudy admired the handiwork with a smile. "Very pretty. What colour will you make the other one?"

"Yellow, I think, then you'll be able to tell which is which."

Her daughter gave her a loving kiss. "Oh, Mum, it's lovely to see you perking up again! It's a miracle."

Mrs. Lawson put down her knitting with a thoughtful air. "Yes, it is a miracle, I think. It happened last night."

Trudy sat down on the chair beside the bed. "Tell me all about it."

"Well, as you know, I've been very far down. The nurses were quite worried about me, for I didn't seem to be responding to treatment. Seeing them worried made me all the more despondent. When you're physically weak like this, you can get very low in spirit, Trudy."

"So I believe, though I've never seen you that way before, Mum."

"I've never been that way before," replied the other. "It puzzled and depressed me. Well, my nurse came along last night and did her best to cheer me up, but it was no good. Then she asked if I wouldn't like the earphones on to listen to the wireless? I wasn't much caring, but she fitted them on and—some providence was working, Trudy. They were singing hymns, and the one I heard was one we know very well 'Safe in the arms of Jesus'."

"Oh, that one," remarked Trudy.

Her mother smiled. "You don't think much of it? Well, I admit it hasn't much appeal for young folk rejoicing in their health and strength. It's a hymn for the insecure and the elderly, and above all for the sick."

"Yes, I can understand that," agreed her daughter.

"Think of it, Trudy. I was lying here, tired and ill and so afraid. It was a nameless fear, I can't explain it. Then that sweet old tune came through to my ears, so soothingly. Do you remember the words?"

Trudy repeated them softly:

"Safe in the arms of Jesus, safe on his gentle breast,
There by his love o'er shaded, sweetly my soul shall
rest."

"They brought me untold comfort," her mother went on. "I just let myself relax, feeling most truly that I was in His arms. Then something seemed to flow through me, a healing power. Ping would understand. He felt the same thing when his 'miracle' happened. So you see I'm all right now, quite all right." Her voice held a joyous conviction.

Trudy gripped her hand. "I'm so glad, Mum!"

"Soon I'll be back among you," declared the invalid. "How are things? Are the workmen still in the house?"

"Unfortunately, yes, but we'll get rid of them before you come back. Derek's cough is better and the twins are in high spirits again. I wish I could bring them to see you, but they would disorganise the whole hospital."

"Yes, I'd love to see them, but I must say I am very well visited. The family is rallying round splendidly and

128

the get-well cards I receive from the folk at the mission would make a picture gallery in themselves!"

"I'm so glad the family are all so near at hand," remarked Trudy.

"Yes, you managed that very well," was the smiling reply.

"Me? I did nothing. It was just the way it happened. Derek and I first, then Esther and David and their two, then you and Ping, and now Nancy and Roy."

"Not forgetting the twins—a nice round dozen!"

When the bell rang for the visitors to leave, Trudy got to her feet. "The time's always so short! But though I've got to go, David will be coming tonight. It's his turn."

"Poor David, I'm sure hospital visiting is not his line of country. He ought to be excused."

"Not at all. But don't be surprised if he turns up in his overalls, with clay in his beard!"

On the way home, she began to wonder if David might by chance forget that it was his 'turn'. You simply could not depend on him these days, and Mum would be so disappointed if he failed her. In the evening, therefore, she phoned Two Ways to remind him.

It was a good thing she did, for he was on his way out to visit his beloved pottery, said Esther.

"Catch him quick! It's his night to visit Mum."

A minute later David's voice came through: "Thanks for reminding me, Trudy. I'll go straight to the hospital now and call in to see you on my way back."

He was as good as his word and Trudy opening the door to him, was glad to see there was no clay in his beard, though she saw traces of it on his shoes.

"Welcome, stranger!" she greeted him. "You'll have to come into the kitchen, I'm afraid. Derek's gone to bed and I'm making some tea. Or would you prefer coffee?"

David replied, "Coffee every time. Tea is a woman's drink."

She queried this. "Our workmen love it and they're not women! David, isn't it grand to see Mum so much better?"

They talked about his visit to the hospital and she gave him a stool to sit on while he drank his coffee.

"This is what I like, no ceremony," he remarked. He seemed restless though, and his eyes had an excited gleam in them.

"Trudy, I've got to tell you, I have definitely made up my mind."

"Yes, about what?" she asked, though she knew.

"I've giving up the factory job. I've just got a large order from a shop in Firton. It's my big chance, and I'm going to take it." His face was alight with enthusiasm but there was no answering light in hers.

"Oh, David, please, please take time to think!"

"But I have thought," he said doggedly.

"Not enough, David. It's a question of ways and means. One can't live on air, you know."

He replied huffily—"How like you to say that! As if I didn't know. Esther is quite willing to put up with any inconvenience. It will only be for a short time."

"How do you know? Of course Esther will do anything you wish. She has spoiled you, David."

Frowning at her—"That's one thing YOU never did," he retorted. "You have always tried to boss me around."

His words hurt her. "If I have bossed you, I never meant to, David, and I'm sorry. But haven't I helped you, too?"

He looked slightly abashed. He was remembering the time when their father died and it became necessary for one of them to give up their studies to take a job. Trudy had insisted that she be the one, though her ambitions were as keen as his own. But for her, he could never have started on his career. His voice softened.

"Yes, you have helped me. You understood me once.

Can't you understand me now?"

Pondering with the coffee pot in her hand, Trudy replied: "Yes, I do understand. This love of art fills your life. You want to be free to exercise all your gifts and nothing else seems to matter. I used to feel a little bit of that myself when I tried my hand at writing poetry. How dare anything interfere with genius! But if you take on responsibilities, David, they ought to come first, I'm convinced of that. Esther and the wee ones I mean."

David took this with a glum face. "All very well, but do you think I like this designing job at the factory? It's becoming more and more irksome every day. The new boss doesn't give me the free hand I used to have. It's getting me down."

"Because," his sister pointed out, "you see a way of escape. If there was no alternative, you'd grit your teeth and go through with it."

David took a gulp of coffee. "You talk like a grandmother!"

"It's because I'm fond of you, and Esther is my best friend. You owe money to her father already, David. You don't want to get into worse difficulties? There's Mum to consider, too. I'm sure she'd worry if you gave up your job."

At this, he jumped up and banged his fist on the dresser. "That's right, bring in the whole family! A man can't make a move without involving a whole tribe!"

"Quite true," she told him. "There's a quotation that says the same thing. 'No man is an island—'"

"Oh, you and your quotations!" In a rage he struggled into his shabby raincoat. "I wish I hadn't come here tonight! You've only confused me. Not that it makes any difference, my mind is made up."

He opened the back door, to add: "If you disapprove of me so much I'd better keep out of your way. Goodnight!" and he disappeared into the darkness.

Trudy closed the door and leaned weakly against it. She had mortally offended her beloved brother, yet she had had to speak her mind. Would she become like Mrs. Scott Brown some day, so blunt and outspoken she frightened people off? It was a thing she would have to watch. Still, she was David's sister and he had always turned to her for advice. This time he was determined not to take it. A bleak outlook for his wife and family!

For once, Nancy was in her element in her own house. Mrs. Melrose had a headache and was keeping to her room, so her daughter-in-law had the kitchen to herself while cooking the midday meal. It was lovely to feel free to make experiments, even if it meant a little untidiness.

There was a special pudding in the oven topped with meringue, the pot roast was at the point of perfection, the sauce was made and the plates were piping hot. Nancy, having poured the potatoes, proceeded to mash them with quick rhythmic movements, while humming a tune. In the dining-room next door the table was laid ready, and the hatch between was open so that the plates could be passed through.

If only this was a meal for herself and Roy alone, she would look forward to it more. Roy wasn't really so finicky about his food as his mother made out. In fact, there were times when he hardly noticed what he was eating, for he had started writing that book and his thoughts were very much elsewhere.

Suddenly her quick movements jerked to a standstill. Roy's mother had come into the kitchen and was peering into the sink.

"Nancy, how untidy! There's a container for the potato peelings—"

"Yes, I know," said Nancy in even tones, "but some of them escaped into the sink." She added to herself, "Careful, Nancy! 'Whoso keepeth his mouth and his tongue'—"

Mrs. Melrose lifted the lid off the pot roast. "M'm, that smells good. What have you to go with it?"

"Cauliflower and white sauce," was the reply. "Potatoes too, of course."

"So I see. Did you put a little milk and a piece of butter in, before you mashed them?"

"Sure," said Nancy, "and some pepper, too."

"Pepper! But my dear girl, Roy never has pepper in his potatoes."

"Well, he's going to have it this time," said Nancy.

The other stiffened. "He'll suffer for it, you know!"

"I don't think so. Roy's stomach is quite normal, really. Would you please move aside a little? Just till I dish the potatoes."

Mrs. Melrose stepped aside. "Nancy," she asked, "is that a broken plate in the bucket?"

Nancy's heart fell. She was so hoping not to be found out.

"I'm afraid it is. I'm very vexed about it."

"One of Aunt Charlotte's Crown Derby plates!"

Nancy wearily pushed back a lock of her dark hair, and said: "They're not Aunt Charlotte's plates any more. They're ours. Roy's and mine."

There, it was out, what she had been longing to say for ages. Mrs. Melrose flushed. "They've been entrusted to you. It seems you don't value them properly."

"But I do! It's just that I feel nervous about them, knowing what you'll say if anything happens. Please, Mrs. Melrose, will you go into the dining-room, and give me more room to work?"

The other drew herself up. "Perhaps you would like me to keep out of the kitchen altogether!"

The temptation was too great. Quietly but firmly, Nancy replied:

"Yes, I would, if it's all the same to you."

In high dudgeon, Mrs. Melrose stalked out of the room.

133

The fat was in the fire now, thought Nancy, aghast at her own temerity. Her mother-in-law would go straight to Roy and complain again. It was hopeless, absolutely hopeless. She would never get on with Roy's mother if she continued to interfere like this; it wasn't in human nature to stand it!

What Nancy did not know was that Roy had been in the dining-room all this time and had overheard the kitchen conversation through the open hatch. It disturbed him greatly, especially after what Trudy had said to him. He had been putting off doing anything about it because, like most men, he hated scenes.

Roy's only fault was a lack of decision. If you let things take their course, they would often clear up by themselves, that was his theory. But Trudy was right. He was Nancy's husband and her happiness should come first with him. He had just come to this conclusion when his mother swept into the room.

"Oh, you are here, Roy." She glanced at the table with its white cloth and shining cutlery. "I'm afraid I don't feel like lunch today. Nancy has just been very rude to me. Practically ordered me out of the kitchen!"

Roy gazed at her, sadly and steadily, "I think you deserved it, Mother."

Her face coloured up. Then she noticed the open hatch. "So you heard what went on? You were not meant to."

"I could not help it, Mother."

"Well then, I hope you'll agree that your wife owes me more consideration than she showed just now!"

"Perhaps," replied Roy, "it is you who should show consideration. Your intentions are good, Mother, but I think a young wife ought to have more freedom in her own kitchen."

It took some courage to speak like this, for he had never found fault with his mother before. She could hardly believe her ears.

"That girl has turned you against me, Roy. I knew it would happen!"

"Not at all," he declared. "Nancy has made no complaint. It is you who have done the complaining."

"Because I've had reason to!"

Roy sighed. "I'm sorry to have to speak like this, but I'm sure you will understand. Nancy is an independent sort of girl; she'd be far better left alone to make her own mistakes."

But his mother did not even try to understand. "You want me to leave you both on your own then? To get out of this house?"

"Of course you must not leave! The house is big enough for us all. Come, let's have our meal. Forgive and forget—"

But she turned away from his outstretched hand. "I don't feel like eating. Indeed I feel very unwell. I'll go up to my room again, and stay there."

Nancy, hearing it all in the kitchen, stood transfixed. To think of Roy sticking up for her like that, it was too good to be true. And now, here he was beside her, holding out his arms.

"Nancy, my love, come and be kissed!"

The serving spoon in her hand went clattering into the sink as she threw herself into his embrace.

"Oh, Roy, thank you, thank you! You still love me, then?"

"More than ever." His cheek was against her hair. "You are a wonderful wife and I adore you."

Nancy was satisfied. No matter what his mother might do or say in the future, she was sure of his love and trust.

17

THE WORKMEN HAD GONE AT LAST. LAST night Derek and Ping had laid the carpet in the big room and replaced the furniture. Today, Trudy planned to vacuum round, polish up, and hang the newly laundered curtains. The day was warmer, but still there was no sign of sun. It had been hidden for a very long time, in more ways than one.

Vacuuming took twice as long with two toddlers to cope with. Matthew kept as far away as possible from the cleaner, for he was not too sure of the noisy big creature, but Mark loved to run in its path and was constantly being tripped. Trudy was halfway through, when the door opened and in walked Nancy.

"Hello, there," she said. "Getting ready for the invalid's return? Don't let me interrupt."

Trudy switched off. "Only too pleased! It's time for elevenses, anyway. Come on." Each scooping up a twin, they made their way to the kitchen.

"Well," asked Trudy when the coffee was ready, "how are things at Broomfield since Roy's eyes were opened?"

"Much better between Roy and me," she replied. "But his mother has taken to her bed and will hardly speak to us."

"Is she really ill, Nancy?"

"I'm not sure. Roy got the doctor yesterday and it seems there's nothing organically wrong. He has given her a nerve tonic. Roy blames himself, of course, for speaking to her like that."

Trudy, who had heard the whole story, suggested that

136

Mrs. Melrose might have an attack of 'the sturdies'. "What we used to take in Becky's days, when we didn't get our own way."

"Hush, I daren't suggest it. In any case, I'm sorry for her, Trudy. She thinks I've come between her and Roy. She gave up her home for his sake—though she needn't have—and now she's a stranger in a strange land."

"If you're sorry for her, that means you've forgiven her," mused Trudy.

"Yes, I have. If only we could have a better understanding! But I can't get close to her. I wish you would come and see her, Trudy."

"Me? I'll try, then. Will tomorrow do? If the weather improves it will do the children good to get out."

"Grand! By the way, have you seen David lately? He seems to be keeping out of my way."

"Mine, too," was the sad reply. "I told him what I felt about him throwing up his job. Has he done it yet, do you know?"

"No idea. Haven't you seen Esther either?"

"No, and she seems a bit short on the telephone. I'm worried about it, Nancy."

Her sister in her capable way was gathering the empty cups to wash them. "The Lawsons can't afford to quarrel, especially when Mum's been so ill. There must be no disharmony when she comes home, Trudy. Everything in the garden has got to be lovely!"

Trudy looked out to the garden with its bare trees and stricken shrubs. It looked as if it would never bloom again. Yet she knew that there was hidden life there, life that would burst joyously forth in the next few weeks.

When Nancy went away she finished the vacuuming, then gave the twins their meal and put them upstairs for a nap. Snatching a lunch for herself, she proceeded to polish up the furniture—piano, sideboard, table and chairs, till everything was gleaming like new. All except the windows, and they could certainly do with a wash! With a pail of water and the long window brush, she went outside and began the task. It was one which she always enjoyed, splashing the water up and watching it glissading down the panes in long cascades.

Absorbed, Trudy suddenly became aware of a small dog snuffling round her feet and making little darts at the dripping brush.

A voice called sharply:

"Jackie! Come here at once!"

She looked round and there was Mrs. Rice at the gate. The two had not come face to face since Trudy had visited the Bank house in an effort at reconciliation. With no hesitation she put down the brush and went forward.

"I'm so glad you've decided to call, Mrs. Rice!"

"But I haven't," was the straight reply. "I was passing and Jackie ran in."

"I see." Trudy noticed that the banker's wife was looking pale and thin, a mere shadow of her former self. "Haven't you been well, Mrs. Rice?"

"I've had influenza." Mrs. Rice explained. "It's been a terrible winter. Nobody came near me."

"I'm sorry. Perhaps nobody knew. Hetherton is a friendly place."

"I haven't found it so," was the reply. Trudy was not surprised. To gain friends one had got to show friendliness. Impulsively she went on:

"As you are here, won't you come in anyway?"

The other hung back. "But you are working. No, thank you, it's time I was on my way home," and she called for Jackie once again.

But Jackie was a law to himself. Seeing the open door, he had run inside.

"There," said Trudy, "he's leading the way. Come, you've been ill and you need a rest."

She gave in—"Well, for a little while—"

In the room, she sank down gratefully on a chair. The cleaning materials were still there and Trudy apologised for them, saying:

"We've had dry rot and the workmen have just finished. I'd like you to have met my mother, but she's in hospital just now."

Mrs. Rice said she was sorry. "Will she get home soon?"

"We're hoping so." As she spoke there were unmistakable sounds from above. The twins were awake. Excusing herself, she went upstairs to collect them and brought them into the room. Matthew at once hid his face shyly against her, but the bold Mark went up to Mrs. Rice and smiled at her. He even condescended to pat the little dog.

"Shake hands, Mark," said his mother, and his fat little hand was placed in the visitor's with the utmost confidence.

"Nice lady," he lisped, the little flatterer!

Trudy took Matthew with her to the kitchen, leaving Mark with the 'nice lady'. Every moment she expected to hear howls and was prepared to rush to the rescue, but while she boiled the kettle for a cup of tea, everything remained very quiet. Coming back with a tray set with cups and cakes she peeped in, then halted, amazed. Mrs. Rice had taken Mark up on her knee. One arm was clasping him tightly and she was stroking his silky hair with an expression on her face which changed it wonderfully. Instead of petulance and discontent, there was a womanly warmth there which must have been long hidden.

Seeing Trudy, she coloured and half ashamedly put Mark down on the floor.

"He's a sweet little thing," she murmured. "I wouldn't mind having a child like that. We lost our baby you know, James and I. Nothing has been the same since." A tear gleamed in her eye which she wiped off self-consciously. "Silly of me to cry."

Trudy set down the tray. "I don't think it's silly. We've

got to cry sometimes; it's a release. I'm sorry you lost your baby, Mrs. Rice. I wish I'd known."

"What difference would it have made?" the other asked.

"I might have been kinder to you."

"But you are being kind, taking me in like this, giving me tea."

"There was a time," Trudy explained as she poured out, "when I felt anything but kind. I blamed you for stealing my home, when it wasn't your fault."

The other nodded. "Yes, I understand how you must have felt, though I didn't then. You've been very generous all along, Mrs. Crawford. The people here think a lot of you. Though I don't go out much I can't help hearing praises of you and your family, and the good you do through your mission. You seem a very happy crowd, there."

"Yes, we're happy. Why not join us?" Trudy was encouraged to ask.

"Me? Oh no, that sort of thing is outside my sphere. I'd feel very awkward butting in."

"Why not bring your husband? I'll see to it you don't feel awkward. This Sunday, if you like—"

But she still declined, and after some more conversation, rose to go. At the door Mark said, "Goodbye, nice lady!" and she took him up and kissed him, her face softening as before. At the gate she waved back to him, then set off with Jackie at her heels.

Trudy's spirits had suddenly soared. When Derek came in later, she greeted him with a bearlike hug.

"Oh, Derek you'll not believe it! Mrs. Rice was here. We're the best of pals!"

He loosened her arms with a laugh. "Hi, stop throttling me! So you've made it up with her ladyship. Good for you!"

"It wasn't all my doing," she told him. "Mark played a large part. He's got a fatal charm that infant, something like our David."

140

Derek shook his finger at his son. "Watch it, Mark!" he warned him.

Next day it happened, what they had been longing for. The sun shone forth in splendour, wakening the world from its winter sleep. New daisies blinked gratefully from the grass and the hawthorn hedge was bathed in a shimmer of green.

"For lo," as Trudy quoted at breakfast time, "the winter is past, the rain is over and gone."

"Don't be too sure about that," mumbled Ping as he rose from the table, still chewing.

"Well, it's over in the meantime and I intend to take the twins out today. We're going up to Broomfield."

Early in the afternoon she put the pair in their new push chair and set off up the hill. Nancy met her half-way and helped to push.

"Lovely to see the sun, isn't it?" Trudy pulled off her woolly cap and let her hair go free. "One day like this in spring is worth ten in summer! Nancy, I had a visitor after you left yesterday," and she told her about Mrs. Rice.

"So you've made it up. I'm so pleased, Trudy. I only wish Roy's mother and I could do the same!"

Nancy took charge of the twins while Trudy went up to Mrs. Melrose's room. It was a pleasant room looking out to the lawn, with the sun streaming in. The invalid was sitting up in bed with a book.

"I hope you don't mind a visitor?" Trudy asked.

"Nancy told me you were coming to 'cheer me up'," was the reply. "I'd rather you didn't try."

"Just as you wish." Trudy went over to the window. "The sun makes such a difference, doesn't it? Everything's sparkling."

"It's too bright," was the complaint. "Do you mind drawing the curtains?"

Trudy complied, then came back to the bed. "Are you feeling any better, Mrs. Melrose? I'm sorry you can't get out."

The other replied coldly, "You needn't bother being sorry for me. Nobody else is."

"What makes you say that?"

"Don't pretend you don't know the circumstances. I have no doubt that your sister has made you fully aware of them. I am bitterly disappointed in Nancy. She has no regard for me whatever."

"You're wrong about that," Trudy protested. "She has a very high regard for you."

The other looked disbelieving. "She never shows it, then. I wonder if she realises how much I gave up to come here? Hampstead was my home, always had been. It was a great shock to come north to such a different life. I was never used to the country. I loved to be near London and all its activities."

Trudy said reflectively, "Yes, I can understand that. Remember that time we met in London with Aunt Charlotte? I loved my holiday there and thought it was so good of you to take an interest in a 'country cousin' like me."

Mrs. Melrose gave a slight smile. "Well, it's nice of you to say it. You at least must realise how much I miss the life down there. This place is dead."

Trudy knew very well that Hetherton was anything but 'dead', though perhaps a self-centred stranger might find it so.

"Perhaps if you went back to Hampstead for a little holiday—?" she suggested. "You must have lots of friends there."

"I did have. They may have forgotten me."

"Real friends don't forget. When you are up and about, Mrs. Melrose, will you come and see my mother? She will soon be home from hospital."

"Will she? With my own illness I had forgotten about her. Certainly, if I am able, I shall call."

Downstairs Trudy reported to Nancy. "It's more than the 'sturdies', Nancy. Roy's mother is pining for her old life in Hampstead. Perhaps it has been too big a change for her. I'm sure her intentions were good, but her devotion to Roy has blinded her to everything else. Now that she's not the only one with him, she feels at a loss. She needs other interests but one can hardly tell her that."

"I'd get put in my place if I were to dare," observed her sister. "I simply can't get through to her at all."

Things would certainly run more smoothly if these two did manage to 'get through' to each other. But at the best there was bound to be friction, as long as they were in the same house. A dominating character like Mrs. Melrose would never consent to take second place.

Trudy was still pondering the problem on the way home when she reached the gate of Ardenlea, and stopped short, unable to believe her eyes. There, in its old place beside the hedge was the garden seat! It had come back as mysteriously as it had disappeared.

Hailing it joyously, the twins scrambled out of their pram and ran towards it. Then they were up on it, though Matthew stuck half-way. Trudy helped him, then sat between them with an arm round each, and that was how Derek found them when he arrived home from work.

18

TRUDY WAS PREPARING THE EVENING MEAL next day when the back door opened and in popped Eva.

"Is Ping home yet?" she asked.

"Not yet. I don't expect he'll be long, though. Can you wait?"

Eva sat down on a kitchen stool. "I've just had another letter from my mother, Trudy. She seems to think she can still shake my determination to marry Ping." Her blue eyes were doleful.

"Poor Eva!"

"Not that I'll ever give in, but I'd like to be on good terms with her. Being in love makes you feel like that; there mustn't be a false note anywhere.

"She says she's coming here soon with my stepfather to make me see sense. I'm dreading it, Trudy!"

Trudy opened the oven door to inspect the 'toad in the hole'. Lowering the gas, she enquired, "Why dread it? You believe in Ping; we all do. Your mother's prejudices might melt."

"You don't know my mother," was the gloomy reply.

"Well, stay for tea anyway and talk things over with him. You can also wash the dishes. This is my night at the hospital."

An extra guest meant smaller portions, but nobody complained except Ping. Eva immediately placed some of her own 'toad in the hole' on his plate. He put it back again, but she returned it, and so it went on, till Trudy told them to stop behaving like kids.

"You're engaged. Time you were growing up!"

She left them in the kitchen washing up, and bundling the twins into their night things, she put Derek in charge and set off for the hospital. Her mother was sitting up knitting the last sleeve of the second cardigan, a yellow one. She knitted on, while Trudy dispensed her news.

"Leading item, Mum, is that Mrs. Rice and I are quite chummy now. We've even got our seat back."

Her mother listened to the story with a smile. "So Mark did the trick, did he? I thought there must be some reason for her ill nature, poor woman. I'm glad her soft side has come through before it's too late. And now, what's the latest about Nancy?"

Trudy told her that, too. "There's still that barrier between her and Roy's mother. Do you think it will ever lift, Mum?"

"Only by God's grace," was the reply. "We must hope and pray."

Trudy went on to talk about Ping and his dilemma. "Eva is dreading this visit from her mother. I'm afraid it means more bitterness, unless she gives in, but surely she won't do that!"

"Eva is not strong-minded in herself," reflected Mrs. Lawson, "but her love for Ping will carry her through, I think. Love is the strongest force, after all. Now, what's David doing this weather? He was here last night, but didn't say much. I thought he looked worried. There's nothing wrong, is there, Trudy?"

"Of course there's nothing wrong," she declared and was seeking to change the subject when she saw the ward Sister coming towards them. She was smiling.

"Well, Mrs. Lawson, I have good news for you," she began. "If all goes well, you are to get home on Saturday. Will you be able to fetch her, Mrs. Crawford?"

"Somebody will, you can depend on that!" was the happy response.

The invalid's eyes were sparkling. "Home again, how

lovely. It has been good here, Sister. You have all been very kind. But after all, there's no place like home."

The Sister heartily agreed.

When she got back, Trudy phoned Nancy to tell her the news.

"Saturday? Wonderful! Roy and I will fetch Mum in the car, and you can have everything ready at home."

It was not very easy to phone David with this coolness between them. When she got through, it was Esther who replied. Her voice lacked the old warmth.

"Oh, it's you, Trudy."

"Yes, I just rang to let you two know that Mum is coming home on Saturday."

"Is she really? That's good," said Esther.

"Roy and Nancy are bringing her. You'll be down to see her, Esther?"

"I expect so," was the reply. "David will, anyway. I'll tell him," and click went the receiver.

Trudy was hurt. How they used to linger on the phone, exchanging confidences. Now it seemed all that was over, but surely not for good?

On Saturday, Trudy made an early start with her preparations. Her mother's room was given a last minute shine, the bed made ready with a new spread and frilled pillow-cases. Fresh nylon curtains framed the window and a big bunch of daffodils from Broomfield made a splash of colour on the dressing-table. The fire in the big room and in fact the whole house seemed to say—'Welcome home!' So thought Mrs. Lawson as she walked slowly in on Roy's arm.

"It's almost worth while being ill to come home to this," she said. "Where are the twins, Trudy?"

"If you're sure you're strong enough, I'll bring them in," said her daughter.

As soon as she was settled in the big chair at the fire, Matthew and Mark appeared.

146

"How big they've grown! I've forgotten which is which."

But she was not long in doubt, for Mark, with a cry of 'Gran-gran!' darted forward.

"It's Mark, of course. Come on, Matthew, don't be shy!"

Thus encouraged, Matthew joined his brother and they were both as good as gold during the meal which Trudy supplied for every one. Then nurse Nancy persuaded her mother to go to bed for the afternoon, promising that she could get up later.

"David and Esther will be looking in, I expect."

While she slept, Trudy said to her sister:

"I hope David does come, Nancy. Surely he wouldn't let the fact that he's annoyed with me stand in the way!"

But Nancy and Roy had gone home, the twins were bedded and still David had not come. Trudy felt herself getting crosser and crosser.

Her mother smiled from her seat by the fire. "I know what you're thinking, that David ought to be here. But he'll come all right, don't worry!"

She was surer of him than Trudy was, but then, she did not know what Trudy knew. She had almost lost hope when the doorbell rang.

"There, you see—" said her mother.

David and Esther were both at the door. "We were waiting for our baby sitter," explained David. "May we come in?"

"Of course, why not?"

"I thought perhaps I wouldn't be welcome," he went on, taking her arm. "I've got to tell you something, Trudy. Owing to your big-sisterly advice, I decided half an hour ago, that I'd stick to my job in the meantime. Does that please you?"

"Please me!" She gave him a hearty kiss. "Esther, did you have a hand in this?"

"No, Trudy." She smiled tremulously. "You know I

147

always go along with David. We talked it out before we came, and he decided."

"I felt," put in her husband, "that I couldn't face you and Mum with this on my mind. Since you and I had those few words I've been putting off resigning, and now I'm glad. Not that I shan't do it someday!"

"Someday, if you like, as long as it's not now," said Trudy, vastly relieved. She took Esther's hand in hers:

"We're friends again, then?"

"As if we could ever be anything else!"

With a mind at ease, Trudy took them into the room, where her mother received them with open arms.

During her convalescence Mrs. Lawson had many visitors. None of them ever left the house without feeling the better of her company. They came ostensibly to 'cheer' the invalid, but it was they who were cheered.

Nancy arrived one day with Roy and his mother in the car.

"I'm so glad you were well enough to come," Trudy told Mrs. Melrose. "Mum is in her room. Will you come and have a chat?"

Mrs. Lawson was up and dressed in an armchair, still looking frail, but there was colour in her cheeks and her eyes were bright. She greeted the visitor warmly.

"You have been ill, too, I believe?" said Mrs. Lawson.

"Not really ill, just a bit depressed," was the reply. "I can't explain these attacks. Do you ever feel depressed, Mrs. Lawson?"

"I did in hospital, so I know how it feels. Do sit down, Mrs. Melrose."

She sat down opposite Mrs. Lawson, leaning forward to say earnestly:

"I expect your depression was physical, but with me— well, to be frank with you, Mrs. Lawson, I have lost my bearings. For so long I thought my rôle in life was to

148

look after my son, whom I love deeply."

"Yes, I certainly understand that," said the other.

"Then," Mrs. Melrose went on, "your daughter came, and he does not seem to need me any more."

Mrs. Lawson put her hand over hers. "He still needs you, but in a different way," she said softly. "There are so many ways of showing love. You can smother a person with kindness or you can give deep thought for what is best for their happiness. The last way is best, I think."

Her visitor, musing over this, got up restlessly and went over to the window. The twins were out there in the garden, and Roy was enjoying himself with them in a way that amazed her. She had never seen him like this before.

" 'What is best for their happiness'," she repeated. "Roy ought to be very happy, Mrs. Lawson, but it has dawned on me lately that my presence in the house is preventing that. But what can I do? Leave him and Nancy on their own?"

"You are the best one to answer that," said her companion.

She took a deep breath. "You are right, and I know what the answer ought to be. But it's a step I don't think I have the strength to take."

"There is One who can help," she was reminded.

"I know what you mean. I believe in God, as you do, and I know the value of prayer. Perhaps I haven't prayed enough. I shall have to try again."

They went on talking for a while and when the visitor rose to leave, she said sincerely:

"I am glad to have had this talk with you, Mrs. Lawson. You have helped me. Trudy was helpful, too. She is a very sensible young person."

"And so is Nancy," remarked her mother with a smile. "Impulsive and self-willed, but good at heart, I assure you. Otherwise your son, who is a wise man, would never have married her."

It was a new thought for Mrs. Melrose. "Yes," she admitted, "I am sure he made a good choice. Nancy and I haven't quite pulled together, but I may have been partly to blame."

It was a Saturday again. Ping was at home and Eva came to have lunch with them. These two saw little of each other except at weekends, for Ping was due to sit exams and spent all his evenings studying.

The meal was no sooner over than the busy doorbell claimed attention. "More visitors for Mum," sang out Trudy as she went to answer it. There was a car at the gate and two strangers on the doorstep, a tall, ageing man and a slender woman with dark hair, dressed rather lavishly in the height of fashion. Looking again, Trudy recognised her. It was Eva's mother, Mrs. Woodrow.

"Mrs. Crawford?" she began. "I saw you on my last visit here. You were in the Bank house then."

Trudy recalled the visit well. The lady had been scornful of everything in Hetherton and for a time had stolen Eva away from them. Her mission today was no mystery. She had come prepared to do her utmost to separate Eva and Ping.

"Yes, I remember you," observed Trudy.

"This is my husband." Her companion bowed gravely. "We called at the Coopers' house and were told Eva was here. We should like to speak to her."

But Eva had overheard. She came into the hall, followed by Ping.

"Hello, Eva, my darling," said her mother, kissing her. But Eva drew back.

"Mummy," she said firmly, "kissing is no use. Please understand, I meant what I said in my letters. Ping and I are engaged, and that's that. You've never met Ping, but here he is now."

Standing very straight and tall, Ping held out his hand.

"I am pleased to meet you and your husband, Mrs. Woodrow."

They shook hands and Trudy opened the room door. The table had just been cleared and Derek had taken the twins out to the back garden. Mrs. Lawson had gone to her room and the place was empty.

"I'll leave you four to talk things over," she said and made her escape.

In the kitchen washing up, she began to wonder what was going on in there. It was obvious from the look Mrs. Woodrow had given Ping that she was not impressed. Lanky and still very youthful looking, Ping was tousled as to hair and his features were not his best point. It was his merry eyes and frank smile that made people love him. But even had he been as handsome as Apollo, he would not have appealed to Eva's mother. Money and influence were what weighed with her and Ping had neither.

Trudy was drying the last dish, when to her consternation the bell rang again. More visitors—how very awkward!

She hurried to the door. There was another car at the gate now, but she wasted no time looking at it for Brian Clyde and his wife Olivia were there, smiling at her. She had written to them about her mother's illness and they had come all the way from Martonbury to see her.

Brian Clyde, the artist preacher, had been the Lawsons' hero since that island holiday long ago, when they had first heard him preach. When Brian and Olivia came on the scene, everything glowed with a kind of magic. They were so special, not like ordinary people at all.

Trudy threw the door wide. "Come in! Come in! Now that you're here, everything's going to be all right!"

Olivia asked, amused, "What makes you think that?"

"Because it always is," declared Trudy.

Then she opened the door of the big room and looked in.

19

SILENCE FELL IN THE ROOM WHEN TRUDY opened the door. Mr. Woodrow was standing glumly at the window, his hands in his pockets. Eva was sitting on the arm of Ping's chair, her face hidden on his shoulder, weeping. Her mother had been addressing the pair in scathing tones and her features were flushed and angry. When she turned and saw the strangers at the door, she controlled herself with an effort, forcing a smile.

"Here are two friends of ours," announced Trudy. "Mr. and Mrs. Brian Clyde."

Leaping to his feet with his arm still round Eva, Ping greeted the newcomer while Eva dried her tears.

Explained Trudy, "Eva and Ping are engaged now, Brian. I think I mentioned that in my letter. These are Eva's parents, Mr. and Mrs. Woodrow."

The two couples shook hands, then Brian turned to the young ones.

"Congratulations, Ping and Eva! Olivia and I always hoped you two would come together. Mr. and Mrs. Woodrow, I must congratulate you, too. Eva is marrying into a very fine family."

"Really? I'm pleased to hear it," Mrs. Woodrow's tones were cool.

"As for Ping—or should we call him Peter? He's got a great future, that young man."

Eyebrows raised—"In what way?" asked Eva's mother.

"He's already got a degree, and soon will have another. A coming young preacher with the gift of eloquence."

Ping blushed, "Brian, please!"

Mrs. Woodrow's only response was a dry, "Oh—a preacher." But her husband turned to Brian with interest.

"Taking about preachers, can it be that you are Brian Clyde, the Artist Preacher?"

"He is," put in Trudy eagerly. "You must have heard of him?"

"I was looking at one of your paintings in a London gallery the other day," said Mr. Woodrow. "Since I retired, I have taken an interest in art and I specially admire your work. But with such a gift, why do you waste time in preaching?"

Brian gave him a straight glance. "Waste of time—doing God's work?"

The other, slightly taken aback, replied:

"Depends on your point of view, I suppose. Frankly, my wife and I don't approve of Eva's engagement to this young man. We want her to have a position in life."

"She will have that," said Brian. "As Peter Lawson's wife, she will be loved and respected. He may well become a powerful influence, but apart from that, if they are happy in their love, what more can you ask?"

At this Mrs. Woodrow spoke out. "You paint a glowing picture of the young man, Mr. Clyde, but as a friend, aren't you prejudiced in his favour? I'd like more proof of his so-called gifts."

Everybody was looking at Ping, who was very pale, his eyes bright with tension. It was Trudy who answered her.

"Ping is due to speak at the mission service tomorrow morning. If you can stay, why not come and hear him?"

The two Woodrows exchanged glances. "There would be no point," Eva's mother replied. "I will never consent to this engagement."

But her husband, respectful of Brian's judgement, put in:

"It can do no harm. We are staying in Firton for the weekend and can easily attend the service."

His wife shrugged. "Oh well, if we can get here in time!"

They took their departure shortly afterwards, leaving a very perturbed Ping.

"I can't go through with this," he told Trudy. "I don't know why you suggested it. How can I be at my best under the circumstances?"

"Forget about the circumstances," advised Brian. "Lose yourself in what you're going to say. You've done it before, you can do it again."

Ping looked at him wanly. "And I was going to ask you to give the address. Won't you, please?"

Brian put his hand on his shoulder. "You have heard me preach often enough. It's your turn now."

Trudy phoned Nancy later that day to tell her about the guests.

"Where are Brian and Olivia staying the night?" her sister asked.

"There's a bed and breakfast place in the village. I'd love to have them here, but there's not enough room."

"Plenty of room at Broomfield! Just send them along," urged Nancy. "And, Trudy, you must all come for lunch tomorrow after the service. It will be a cold meal, for I'll be at the hall, too. Elsa can look after things."

"But Roy's mother—" interposed Trudy.

"She won't mind. Trudy, things look much more hopeful. Mrs. Melrose has got in touch with a friend in Hampstead, a widow like herself. The upshot is that she is going there for a holiday. Later, they may set up house together and Roy's mother will spend the summers with us. Isn't it a marvellous arrangement?"

"It's a very unselfish step for her to take, Nancy."

"I know. She's been different lately. I think that talk with our Mum decided her. Trudy, I actually feel I could love her now, and she is getting fond of me, too; I can hear it in her voice. I am so happy, and so is Roy!"

Trudy hastened to impart to their mother the newest development at Broomfield.

"If one loves enough and prays enough, miracles can happen," was Mrs. Lawson's comment.

Next day, Trudy woke early to a chorus of birdsong mingling with the twitterings of the twins in the next room. At the moment they were happy, but just to be prepared for ructions she got up and dressed, tip-toeing quietly downstairs. When she opened the back door for the milk, the sun came streaming in. Good! It was going to be a perfect day. Sunshine would make a difference to the attendance at the service, though Ping always drew the crowds whatever the weather. Poor Ping—how was he going to stand up to his ordeal? So much depended on it; his whole future, perhaps.

Mrs. Lawson insisted on getting up for breakfast.

"In fact," she remarked at table, "I'd love to go to the service, I've missed so many."

"Why not?" said Derek. "We'll order Tam's taxi and save you the walk. Ping needs it too. His inspiration will have less chance to escape."

Ping, looking distraught and unslept, replied:

"My inspiration, such as it was, has already escaped!"

But Trudy pressed his hand under the table, comforting him as of old.

"Brian has faith in you. We all have. You'll get through, so keep your heart up!"

Peggy Carson arrived to take charge of the twins as usual and the taxi came shortly afterwards. It was a great day for Mrs. Lawson, her first outing since her operation. When they alighted at the hall, she was besieged by enquiries and good wishes. Though a comparative newcomer to the place, she had already inspired much affection.

Before going into the hall, Trudy looked back along the road, for she had spied Mr. and Mrs. Rice leaving their house as the taxi passed. Yes, there they were, making for the hall, but holding back a little, as if unsure. Trudy went to welcome them and Mrs. Rice said, needlessly apologetic:

"It's such a lovely day, and we heard your young brother was going to speak."

"I'm glad you came," was the sincere reply. "And now you can meet my mother at last. She'll be glad to have you beside her." Introductions were made and the others passed in, but Trudy was not ready yet, for the Woodrows had still not come. Were they regretting their promise? Would they go south again without giving Ping his chance?

She could hear the organ playing inside the hall. They were singing the opening hymn:

"My God I thank thee who hast made the earth so bright,
So full of splendour and of joy, beauty and light—"

It was time to go inside. She took a last look along the road, but there was nothing there. Giving up, she was at the door when a car horn made her turn. Sweeping round the corner came the Woodrows' car. It stopped and Eva's parents got out, her mother asking:

"Are we in time?"

"Just," said Trudy. "I've been waiting for you."

With a grimace, Eva's mother said: "I was hoping we'd be too late! Oh well, lead on. In for a penny, in for a pound."

The hall was full, but there was room at the back, so they slipped in, just as the hymn came to an end. After a short prayer Derek announced the second hymn and the Woodrows stood up with the rest, not singing, but looking round with considerable interest.

The good day had brought the women folk out in their spring clothes and the sun shining through the south windows lit up the colourful hues. It shone on Esther's hair as she sat at the organ, turning it to burnished gold. There were three people on the platform—dynamic Brian, older now but still as handsome; Derek, quiet but always dependable, and young Ping, determined that, come what may, he would get his message across to the people.

Trudy prayed silently for him as he rose and faced his audience. He had chosen for his text a verse from the 26th Chapter of Isaiah: 'Trust ye in the Lord for ever: for in the Lord Jehovah is everlasting strength'. For a long moment he stood with his eyes on the listeners as if summoning up courage to speak. Then he straightened himself purposefully, took a deep breath and began.

Ping never 'declaimed'. His aim was rather to appeal, and he made his appeal this morning in a frank, unassuming way.

"I'm going to talk to you today about happiness. It's what we all want, isn't it?" Their interest was aroused, for who could disagree with such an obvious fact?

Ping's next move was to hold up a daily newspaper, known to everybody.

"In this paper I have just read an article dealing with the decline in religious belief and in morals as a whole. People are not as honest as they were, it says; they are more 'permissive'. Anything goes . . . Strangely enough, in this same paper a psychologist tells us that in this country today, people are less happy than they used to be. Though they are better off, they are also more discontented. The writer does not connect this decline in happiness with the decline in religious belief. Nevertheless," and he said the words with conviction—"it is plain to anyone who thinks it out, that the one is the result of the other."

He paused to let his words sink in. They waited.

"We have all got our own ideas about what 'happiness' means," he went on. " 'If only,' we say, 'we had more money, more this and more that, we would be happy.' But would we? Look at the picture of any millionaire. Does he look happy? More likely, he looks burdened with a load of care. For that is what money and possessions bring: worry, fear that you will lose them.

"Or perhaps it isn't money you want," he suggested. "You may be ill and you long to be well. 'If only I could be better of this thing I would be happy,' you say. But when you do get better, something or other comes along and you lose heart again. Or, you may be parted from someone you love. 'If only they were here,' you wish, 'I'm sure I would be happy'—"

They sat listening intently to the simple oration which so reflected their own lives.

"The truth is," Ping argued with growing intensity, "that no one thing can give us lasting happiness. There is always a fly in the ointment. Haven't you found this?"

They smiled, for he only spoke the truth.

"Money," he declared, "can be taken from us. Health can fail and friends can leave us. Surely it is impossible to be happy in a world which is so insecure? But it is not impossible, my friends. It is gloriously possible."

At this point Ping's voice rang out with the conviction which made his preaching so compelling.

"If we put our trust in God and do what He would have us do, misfortunes will not daunt us, and we need not fear the darkest way."

He told them, as they sat there hushed, how by prayer and surrender they could find that perfect trust which would bring the only true happiness. At the end he left them with one simple reminder.

"Once you have got this trust, then, instead of saying 'if only' so often, you will find yourself saying 'even if—'. Even if the worst happens, we are safe, for God is our refuge and our strength."

Ping never said a word too much. Having made his point, he left them to think it out. Short as his address had been, Trudy could see that it had taken a lot out of him. But he was on his feet again to join in the singing of the next hymn. A very familiar hymn, it put into a few words all that he had been telling them.

"*Courage, brother! do not stumble,*
Though thy path be dark as night;
There's a star to guide the humble:
'*Trust in God and do the right*'."

It was a memorable gathering at Broomfield that day. The Woodrows were invited too, and were obviously impressed by the magnificent house and grounds. Trudy guessed what was in their minds. There was wealth somewhere around! Would Eva really do so badly for herself after all? It was the wrong attitude, but how many people besides the Woodrows held it.

Their manner to Ping seemed much softer, even respectful. It was too much to expect that his address had made much impact on them personally for they had listened in a critical frame of mind, but it must have stirred them to some thought, for when they gathered on the lawn after lunch, Eva's stepfather sat down on a deck chair beside Trudy, saying in a friendly way:

"You are a very nice crowd here, I must say. I have enjoyed my visit to Hetherton."

Trudy replied warmly, "Oh, I'm glad. You'll come again, then?"

"Thank you, we probably shall. From the few words I've had with my wife, I gather her objections to Eva's engagement are weakening. I think a lot of your brother, Mrs. Crawford. I'm sure he'll do a great deal of good in the world."

Before they left, Mrs. Woodrow made Ping and Eva very happy by admitting that, as they seemed to be so suited to each other, they might as well have her blessing. Eva kissed her, this time without reserve.

"Thank you, Mummy! I'm glad we're going to be friends. You know now that you can trust me with Ping?"

Then they moved towards their car in the drive, looking back at the people they were leaving, perhaps with a twinge of regret. For never had the Broomfield lawn presented a more smiling scene. Trudy's heart warmed as she glanced from one happy face to another. There was her mother having a heart-to-heart talk with Mrs. Melrose, as they reclined in the lounge chairs specially reserved for the older ones. The youngest were there, too, running around keeping the company on its toes, for Esther and David had come with their two daughters and Peggy Carson had brought the twins.

Close by, Nancy and Esther were discussing new hymn tunes with Olivia, while David and Brian had got into a huddle to talk about things artistic.

And there, walking up the drive arm-in-arm after waving the Woodrows off, came Ping and Eva, their faces shining. Trudy turned to Derek, who was lying stretched out beside her, his face to the sun:

"Derek, if time could stop when we wanted it, I would stop it now."

He sat up, rather dazed, to smile at her. "Why?"

"Because at this moment I'm so happy; everybody's so happy! Before long, something's bound to spoil it."

He nodded. "Sure. Then we'll remember what Ping said. It's to be 'even if', not 'if only'."

His lean brown hand lay on the grass beside her. She traced the veins on the back of it with her finger-tip, feeling she had never loved him so much. He caught her hand and squeezed it.

"You say you're happy, Trudy, yet there's such a lot you haven't got! That car, a house of your own—"

"And such a lot I *have* got," declared Trudy, holding out her arms to the twins as they ran towards her across the grass.